Praise His Majesty

Praise His Majesty

 Psalm Arrangements for Beginning Pianists

by Marilyn DeVries

Reformed Free
Publishing Association

Music simplified from *The Psalter with Doctrinal Standards,*
Liturgy, Church Order, and Added Chorale Section
(Grand Rapids: William B. Eerdmans Publishing Company, rev. ed. [PRC], 1995)

Permission for use of numbers 1–413 from *The Psalter*
granted by William B. Eerdmans Publishing Company,
Grand Rapids, Michigan

Reformed Free Publishing Association
4949 Ivanrest Avenue SW
Grandville, MI 49418-9709 USA
website: www.rfpa.org
email: mail@rfpa.org

ISBN 0-916206-92-0
LCCN 2005933294

Contents

Preface

Throughout my years of giving piano instruction to the children of the church, I have noticed that the goal of most of my students is to be able to play out of *The Psalter*. The idea of writing this book entered my mind when one of my young students asked, hopefully, if the new hymn he was assigned was a tune from *The Psalter*. When I replied that it was not, he sighed deeply and said, "I wish it was." At that point, I was convinced that I needed to put together a book such as this one.

This book contains approximately one-half of the tunes found in *The Psalter*. The most familiar tunes have been included, as well as those which most readily lend themselves to simple arrangement. Songs with difficult timing have been omitted. The beginning piano student will be able to play the first few songs after only a few lessons. The book gradually progresses to levels that are more difficult. Upon completion of this book, the student should be ready to play out of *The Psalter* itself.

Teachers of piano may find this book a worthwhile supplement to their students' course of study. Adults with limited experience on the piano may also find this book to be of value for their enjoyment.

The Psalms are God's own songbook, given to the church throughout the ages. The Psalms are a source of great joy and comfort in every circumstance of life, and they are a vital part of worship. It is my hope that this book will promote the singing of the Psalms, especially in the lives of the covenant children, and that the name of our God will be glorified and praised through its use.

—Marilyn DeVries

Acknowledgements

I am deeply indebted to Elaine Rau, without whose capable assistance, this book would never have become a reality. Her facility at the computer, organizational skills, musical ability, and enduring patience were invaluable. Completing this project was truly a joint endeavor. To Elaine, my sincere thanks.

I am also grateful to Kirsten DeVries, Bonnie Moelker, and Fran Lubbers for their work of editing. The conscientious and painstaking care that they took was made obvious by their constructive criticism and helpful suggestions. I am appreciative of the time and effort they so willingly expended.

The encouragement that I received from my husband, family, and friends during the course of completing this book was greatly appreciated, and I thank them all.

—Marilyn DeVries

The Message of Redemption

Psalm 96
Charles H. Gabriel

Psalter #258

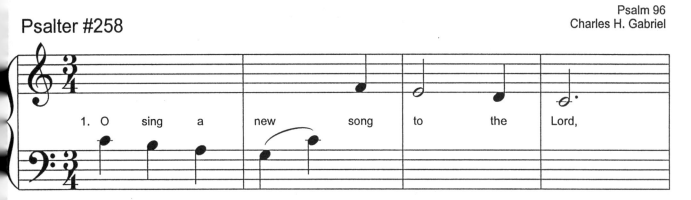

1. O sing a new song to the Lord,

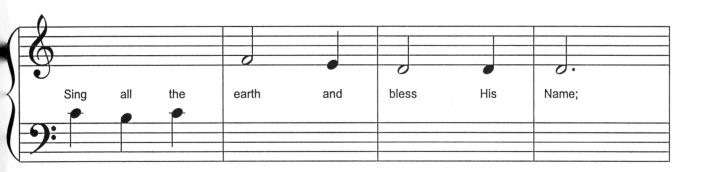

Sing all the earth and bless His Name;

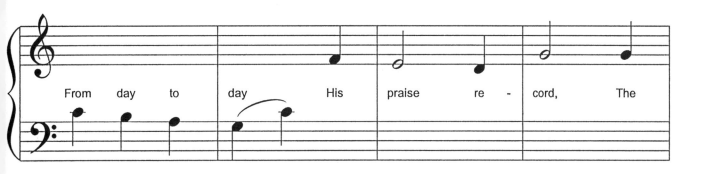

From day to day His praise re - cord, The

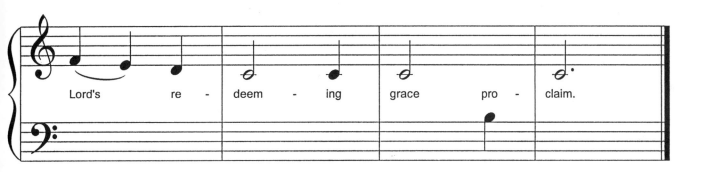

Lord's re - deem - ing grace pro - claim.

-1-

A Salvation for the World

Psalter #262

Psalm 98
Anonymous

1. Un - to God our Sav - iour Sing a joy - ful song;

Won - drous are His do - ings, For His arm is strong.

He has wrought sal - va - tion, He has made it known,

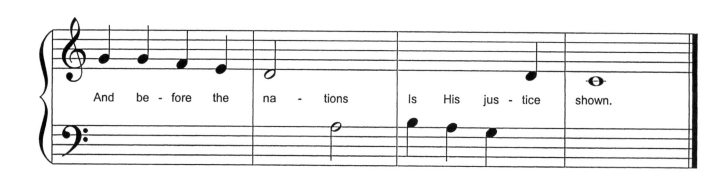

And be - fore the na - tions Is His jus - tice shown.

Missionary Triumphs

Psalter #264

Psalm 98
Arranged from Mehul

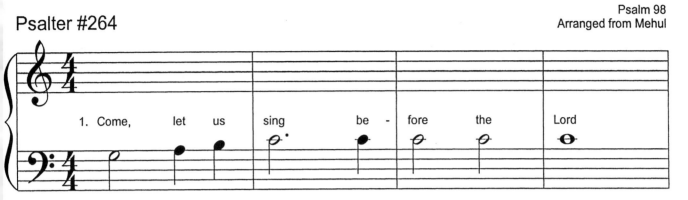

1. Come, let us sing be - fore the Lord

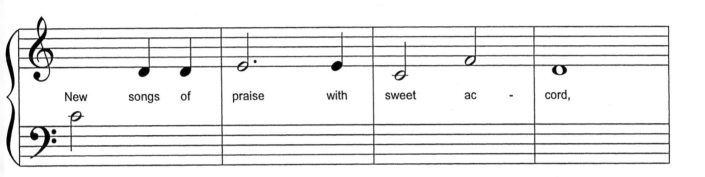

New songs of praise with sweet ac - cord,

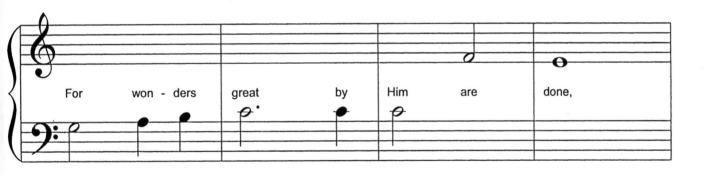

For won - ders great by Him are done,

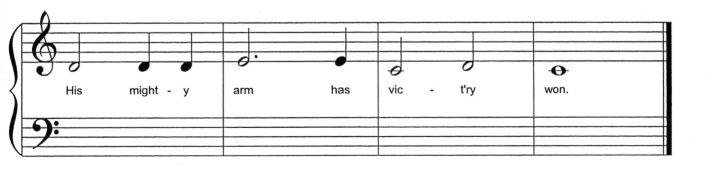

His might - y arm has vic - t'ry won.

The Church and Her Head

Psalm 102
Arranged from Gottschalk

Psalter #276

1. Thou, O Lord, art God a - lone;

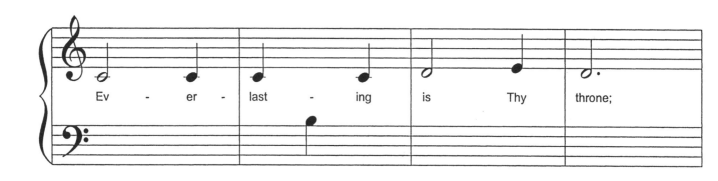

Ev - er - last - ing is Thy throne;

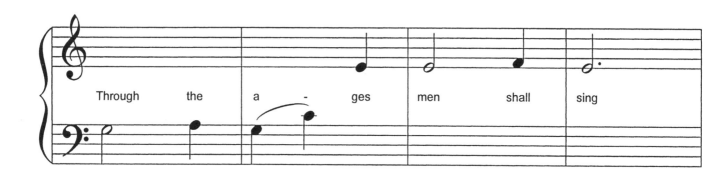

Through the a - ges men shall sing

Praise to heav'n's e - ter- nal King.

The Enlightening Power of the Word

Psalm 119
Theodore E. Perkins

Psalter #334

1. Thy word sheds light up - on my path;

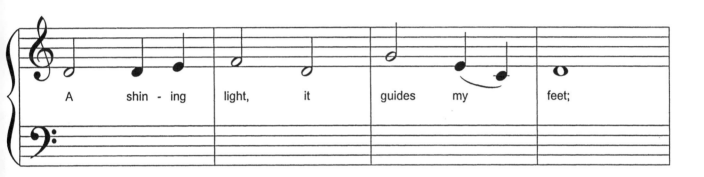

A shin - ing light, it guides my feet;

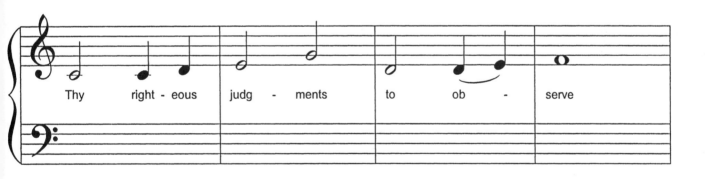

Thy right - eous judg - ments to ob - serve

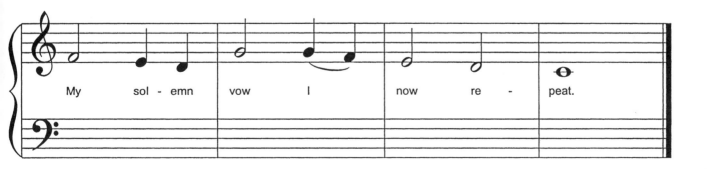

My sol - emn vow I now re - peat.

The Watchful Care of God

Psalm 121
Albert L. Peace

Psalter #347

1. Un - to the hills a - round do I lift up My long - ing

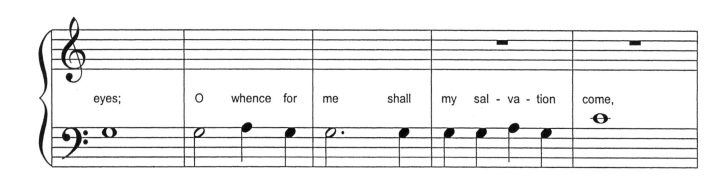

eyes; O whence for me shall my sal - va - tion come,

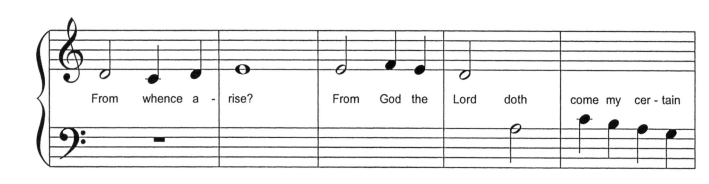

From whence a - rise? From God the Lord doth come my cer - tain

aid, From God the Lord Who heav'n and earth hath made.

Our Only Saviour

Psalm 142
Arranged by Lowell Mason

Psalter #387

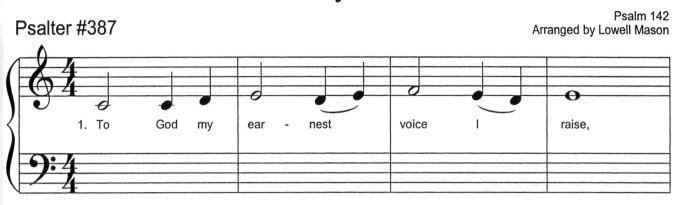

1. To God my ear - nest voice I raise,

To God my voice im - plor - ing prays;

Be - fore His face my grief I show

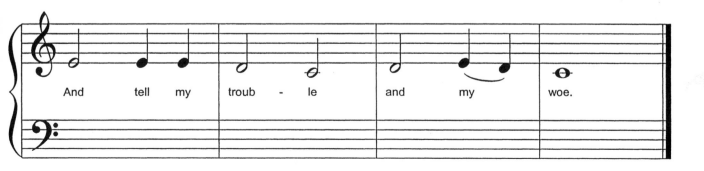

And tell my troub - le and my woe.

God the Only Deliverer

Psalm 33
German Melody

Psalter #87

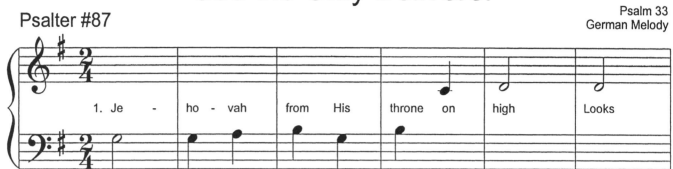

1. Je - ho - vah from His throne on high Looks

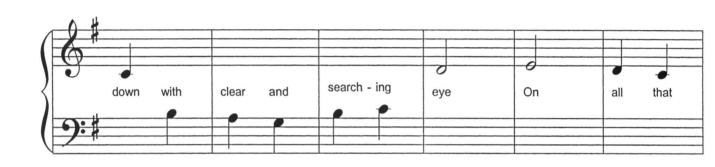

down with clear and search - ing eye On all that

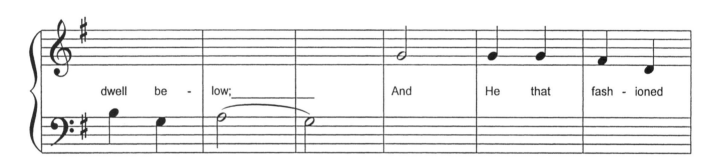

dwell be - low;_____ And He that fash - ioned

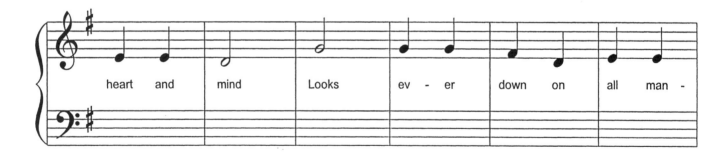

heart and mind Looks ev - er down on all man -

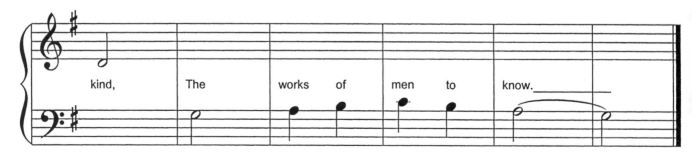

kind, The works of men to know._____

Grace and Gratitude

Psalter #111

Psalm 40
Joseph Barnby

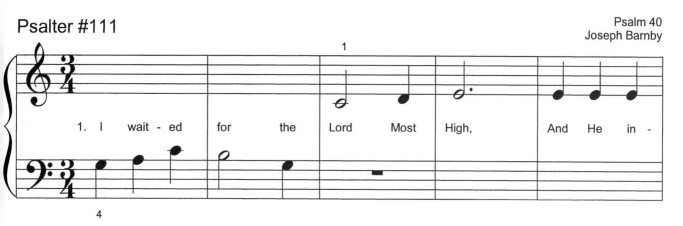

1. I wait - ed for the Lord Most High, And He in -

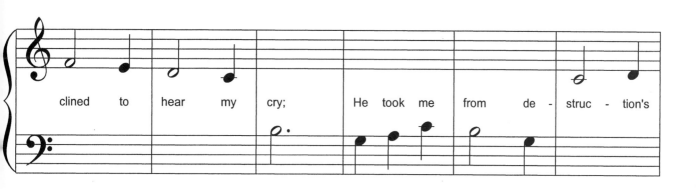

clined to hear my cry; He took me from de - struc - tion's

pit And from the mir - y clay; Up - on a rock He

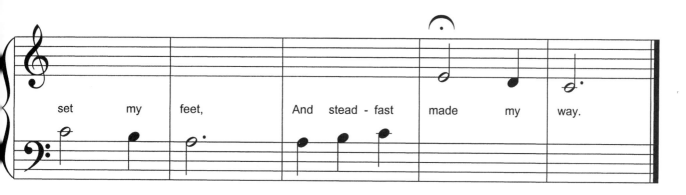

set my feet, And stead - fast made my way.

The Lord Our Shepherd

Psalter #53

Psalm 23
William H. Havergal

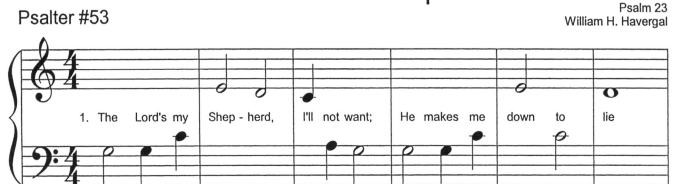

1. The Lord's my Shep - herd, I'll not want; He makes me down to lie

In pas-tures green; He lead-eth me The qui - et wa - ters by.

The Safety of Believers

Psalter #91

Psalm 34
Herbert S. Oakeley

1. God guards the good with watch - ful eye, His ear at -

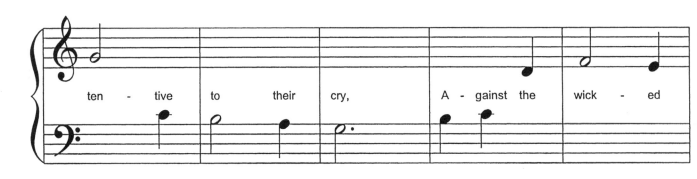

ten - tive to their cry, A - gainst the wick - ed

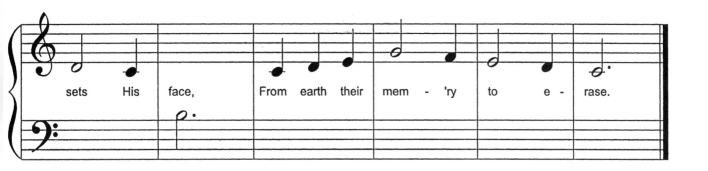

sets His face, From earth their mem - 'ry to e - rase.

Christ and His Cause

Psalm 72
John B. Dykes

Psalter #195

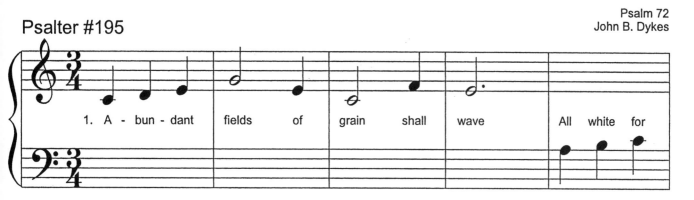

1. A - bun - dant fields of grain shall wave All white for

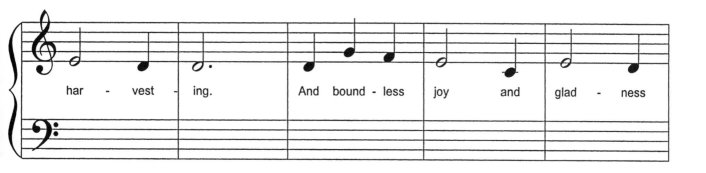

har - vest - ing. And bound - less joy and glad - ness

fill The cit - y of the King.

Guidance and Glory

Psalm 73
E. Grace Updegraff

Psalter #202

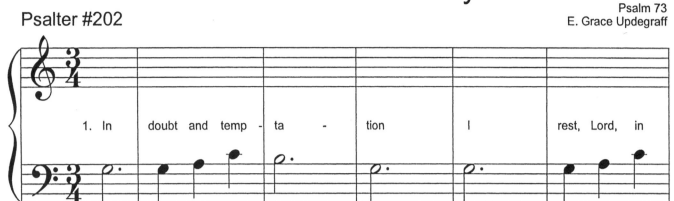

1. In doubt and temp - ta - tion I rest, Lord, in

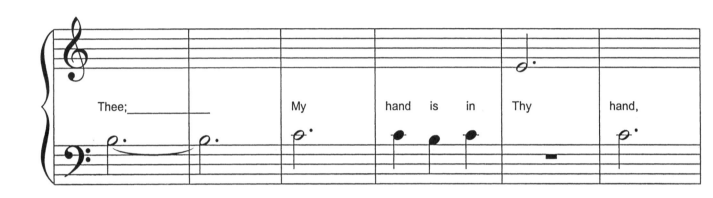

Thee;_____ My hand is in Thy hand,

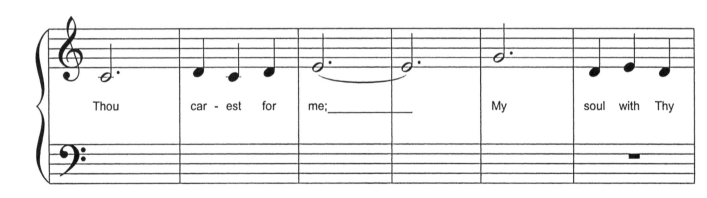

Thou car - est for me;_____ My soul with Thy

coun - sel through life Thou wilt guide,_____

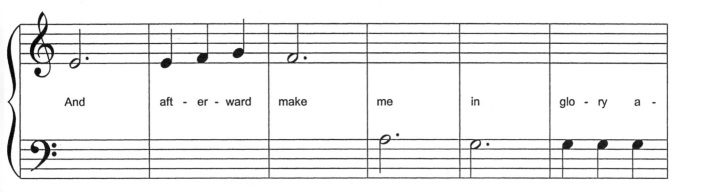

And aft - er - ward make me in glo - ry a -

Chorus

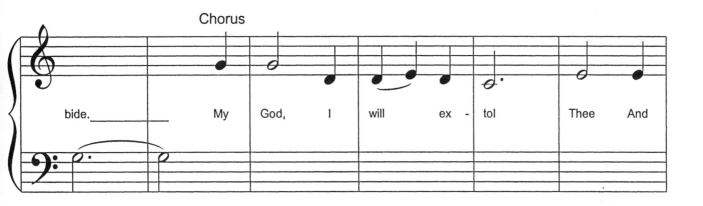

bide._____ My God, I will ex - tol Thee And

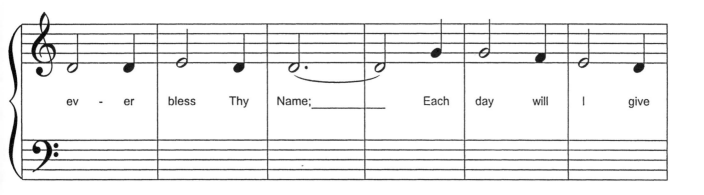

ev - er bless Thy Name;_____ Each day will I give

thanks to Thee And all Thy praise pro - claim._____

Trust and Praise

Psalm 146
Charlotte A. Barnard

Psalter #400

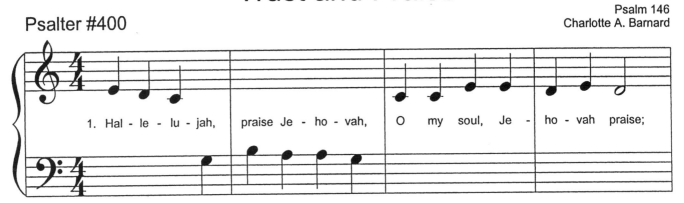

1. Hal - le - lu - jah, praise Je - ho - vah, O my soul, Je - ho - vah praise;

I will sing the glo - rious prais - es Of my God through all my days.

A Cry for Help

Psalm 59
James Walch

Psalter #157

1. Pro - tect and save me, O my God,

From foes that seek my life, And set me high, se -

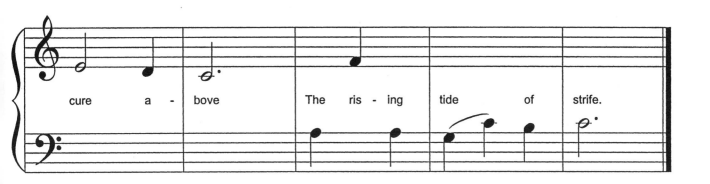

cure a - bove The ris - ing tide of strife.

Harvest Thanksgiving

Psalm 65
Arranged from Johann Stiastny

Psalter #167

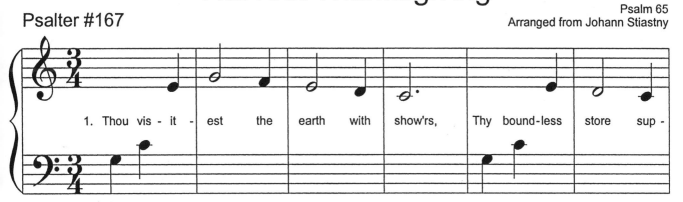

1. Thou vis - it - est the earth with show'rs, Thy bound-less store sup -

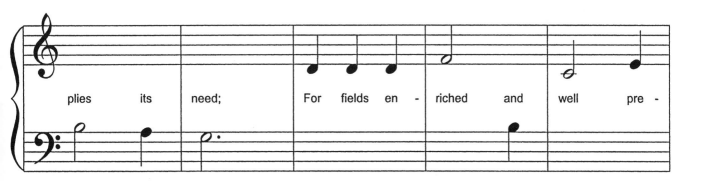

plies its need; For fields en - riched and well pre -

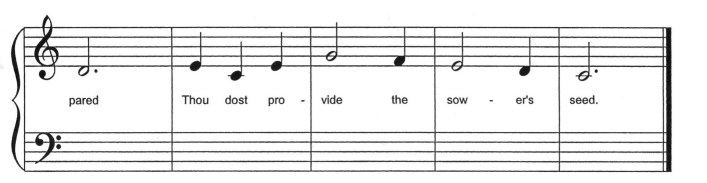

pared Thou dost pro - vide the sow - er's seed.

The Blessed Life

Psalter #305

Psalm 112
H. A. Cesar Malan

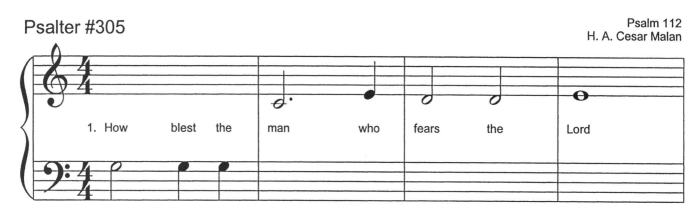

1. How blest the man who fears the Lord

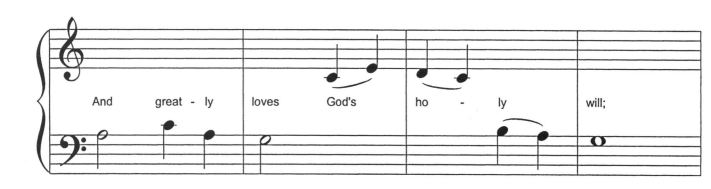

And great - ly loves God's ho - ly will;

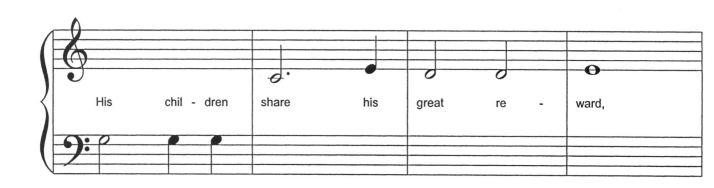

His chil - dren share his great re - ward,

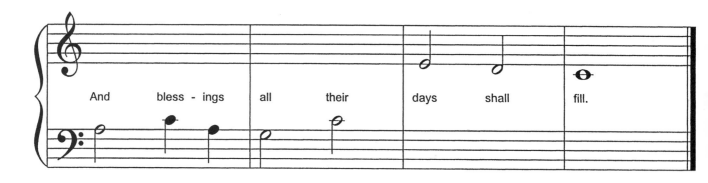

And bless - ings all their days shall fill.

The Lord Our Dwelling-Place

Psalter #245

Psalm 90
Arranged by J. G. Walton

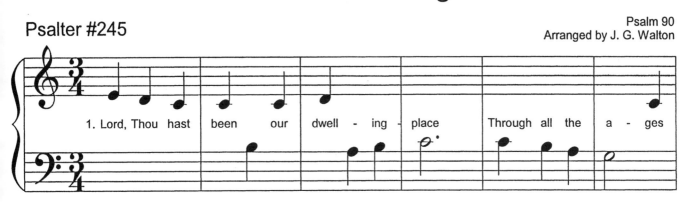

1. Lord, Thou hast been our dwell - ing - place Through all the a - ges

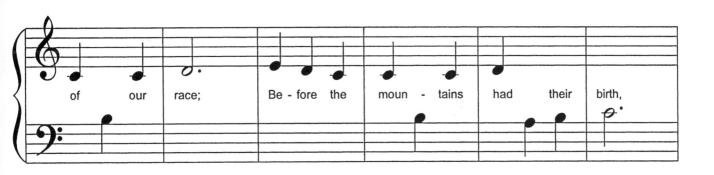

of our race; Be - fore the moun - tains had their birth,

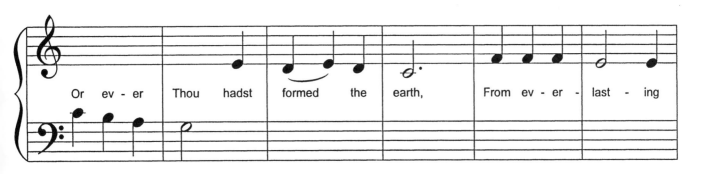

Or ev - er Thou hadst formed the earth, From ev - er - last - ing

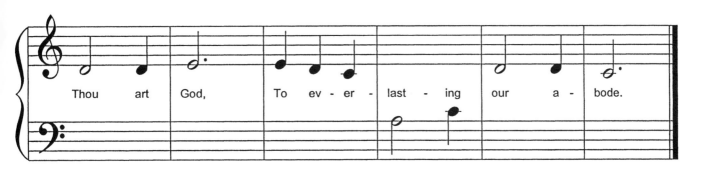

Thou art God, To ev - er - last - ing our a - bode.

The Lord Our Maker

Psalm 139
George J. Elvey

Psalter #383

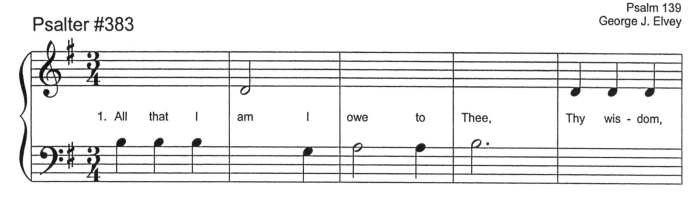

1. All that I am I owe to Thee, Thy wis - dom,

Lord, hath fash - ioned me; I give my Mak - er thank - ful

praise, Whose won - drous works my soul a - maze.

Thanksgiving and Praise

Psalm 100
Genevan Psalter

Psalter #268

1. All peo - ple that on earth do dwell, Sing to the Lord with cheer - ful voice; Him

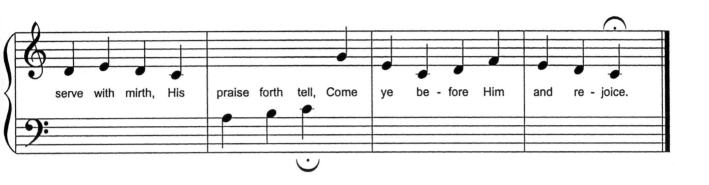

serve with mirth, His praise forth tell, Come ye be - fore Him and re - joice.

Divine Sovereignty

Psalm 97
Frederick H. Burstall

Psalter #260

1. Je - ho - vah reigns; let earth be glad And all the

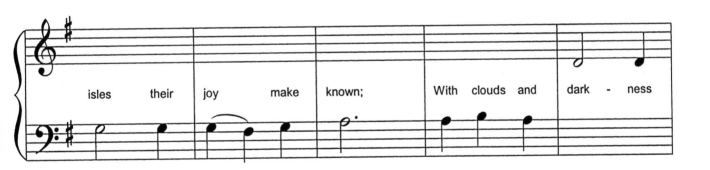

isles their joy make known; With clouds and dark - ness

He is clad, On truth and jus - tice rests His throne.

A Trustful Appeal to God

Psalm 4
William B. Bradbury

Psalter #6

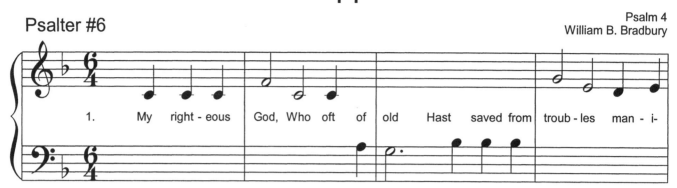

1. My right-eous God, Who oft of old Hast saved from troub-les man-i-

fold, Give an-swer when I call to Thee, Be gra-cious now and hear my plea.

The Prosperity of the Upright

Psalm 37
Lowell Mason

Psalter #101

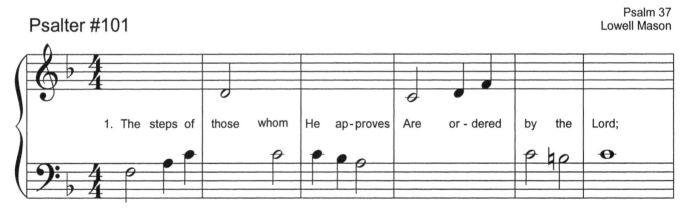

1. The steps of those whom He ap-proves Are or-dered by the Lord;

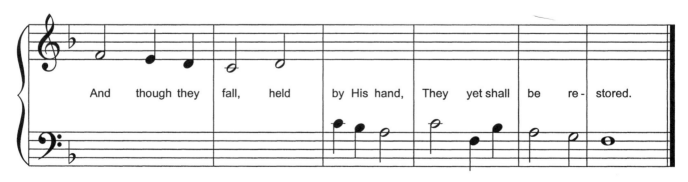

And though they fall, held by His hand, They yet shall be re-stored.

The Marvelous Works of God

Psalm 111
Gardiner's Sacred Melodies

Psalter #304

1. O give the Lord whole - heart - ed praise,

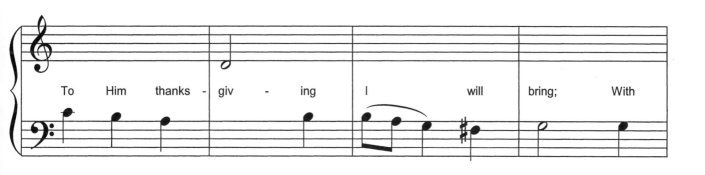

To Him thanks - giv - ing I will bring; With

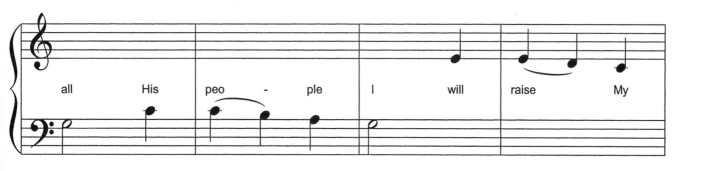

all His peo - ple I will raise My

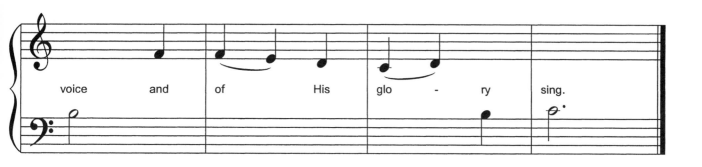

voice and of His glo - ry sing.

Praise for Gracious Deliverances

Psalm 107
William H. Squires

Psalter #294

1. Men who walk in fol - ly's way, And to e - vil turn a - side,

Find that sor - row will re - pay Those who wis - dom's laws de - fied;

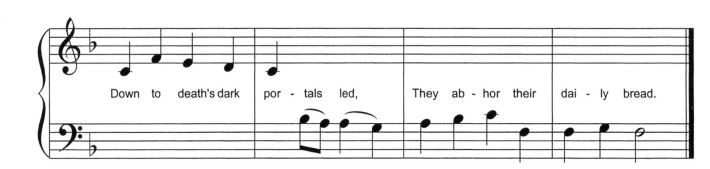

Down to death's dark por - tals led, They ab - hor their dai - ly bread.

Chastened Submission

Psalm 39
Robert S. Ambrose

Psalter #106

1. What wait I for but Thee? My hope is in Thy Name;

From all my sins de - liv - er me, Nor put my soul to shame.

Instruction in the Divine Law

Psalm 119
Joseph P. Holbrook

Psalter #325

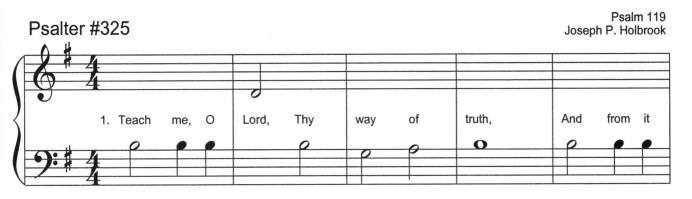

1. Teach me, O Lord, Thy way of truth, And from it

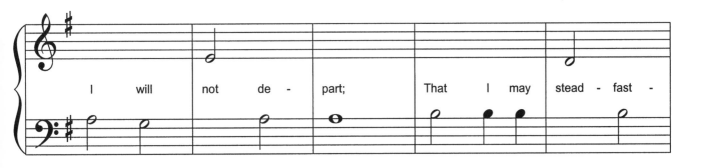

I will not de - part; That I may stead - fast -

ly o - bey, Give me an un - der - stand - ing heart.

The Paths of the Lord

Psalter #68

Psalm 25
Arranged from Cherubini

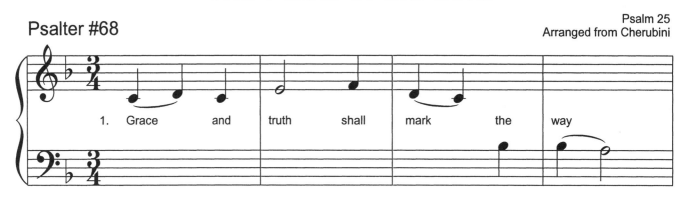

1. Grace and truth shall mark the way

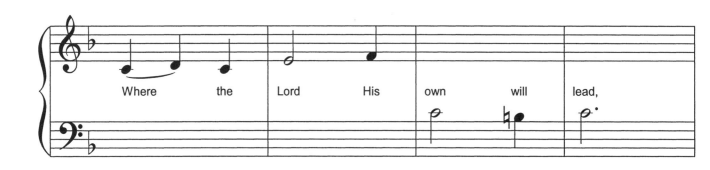

Where the Lord His own will lead,

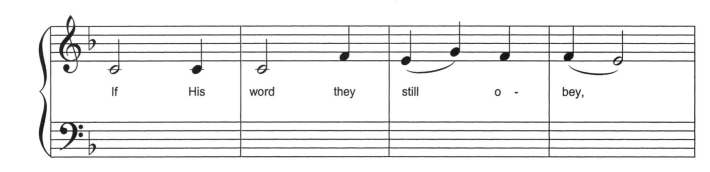

If His word they still o - bey,

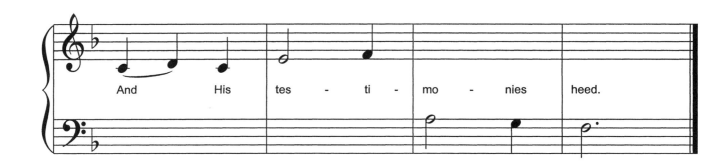

And His tes - ti - mo - nies heed.

The Living Sacrifice

Psalm 116
Benjamin F. Baker

Psalter #311

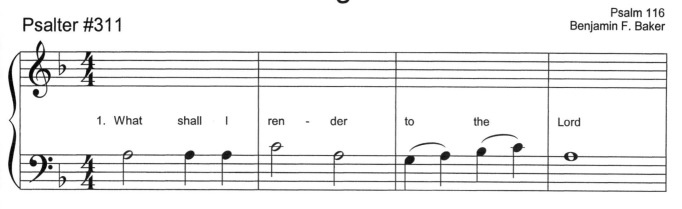

1. What shall I ren - der to the Lord

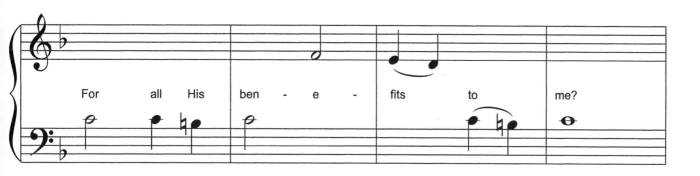

For all His ben - e - fits to me?

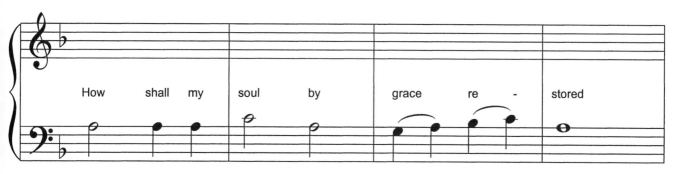

How shall my soul by grace re - stored

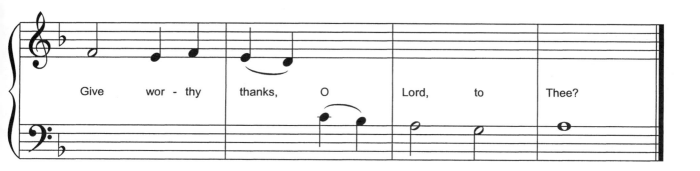

Give wor - thy thanks, O Lord, to Thee?

The Blessings of Grace

Psalm 65
Isaac Smith

Psalter #172

1. Praise waits in Zi - on, Lord, for Thee; There

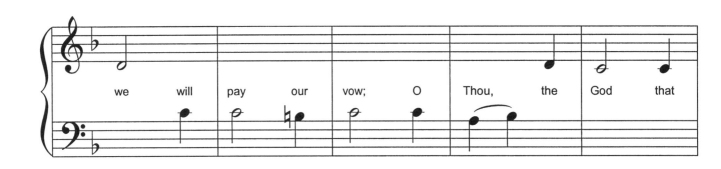

we will pay our vow; O Thou, the God that

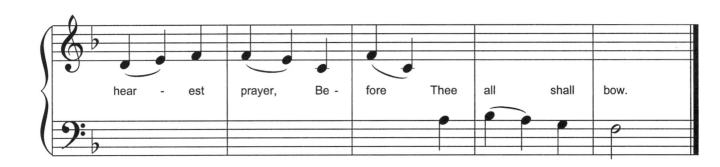

hear - est prayer, Be - fore Thee all shall bow.

Petitions for Deliverance

Psalm 69
Daye's Psalter

Psalter #185

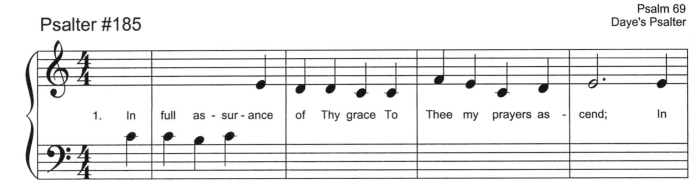

1. In full as - sur - ance of Thy grace To Thee my prayers as - cend; In

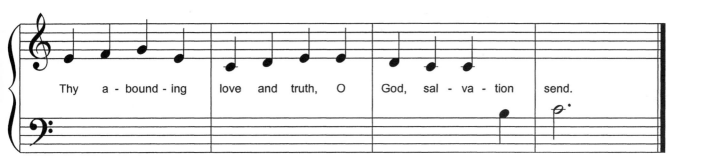

Thy a - bound - ing love and truth, O God, sal - va - tion send.

Divine Grace Magnified

Psalm 65
St. Alban's Tune Book

Psalter #166

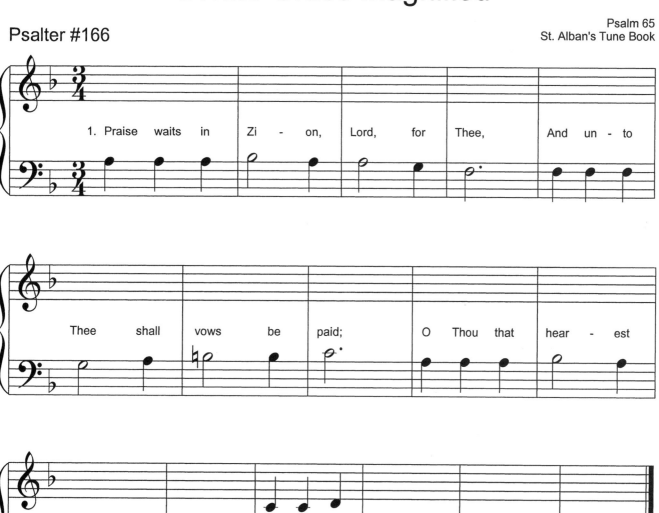

1. Praise waits in Zi - on, Lord, for Thee, And un - to

Thee shall vows be paid; O Thou that hear - est

those who cry, To Thee by all shall prayer be made.

Human Corruption

Psalm 14
William M. H. Aitken

Psalter #23

1. The God Who sits en - throned on high

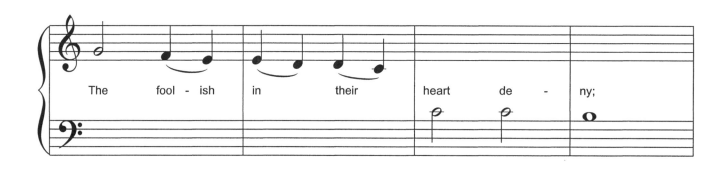

The fool - ish in their heart de - ny;

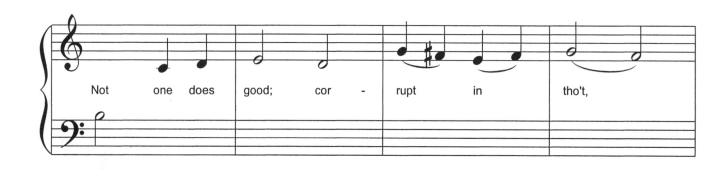

Not one does good; cor - rupt in tho't,

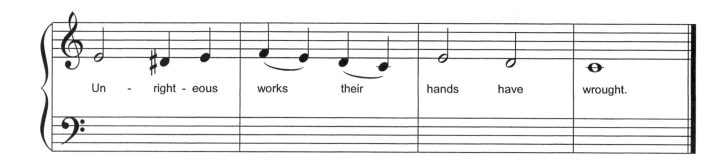

Un - right - eous works their hands have wrought.

The Blessedness of Obedience

Psalm 119
Samuel P. Tuckerman

Psalter #321

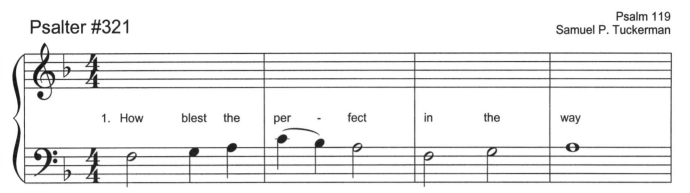

1. How   blest   the   per - fect   in   the   way

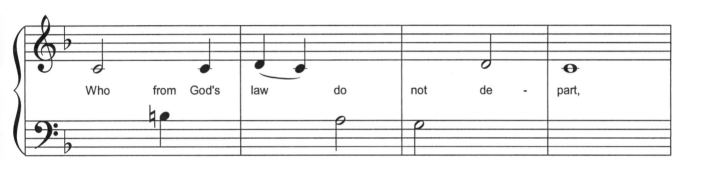

Who   from   God's   law   do   not   de - part,

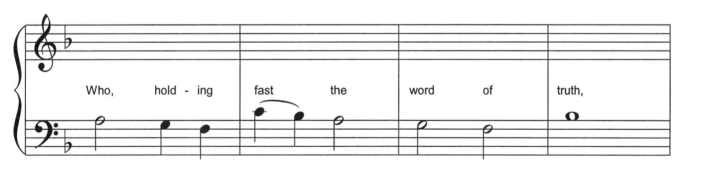

Who,   hold - ing   fast   the   word   of   truth,

Seek   Him   with   un - di - vid - ed   heart.

The Value of Holy Scripture

Psalm 19
George Kingsley

Psalter #41

1. Most per-fect is the law of God, Re - stor-ing those that stray;

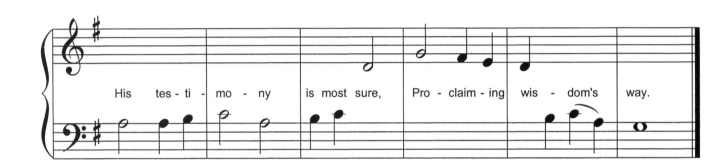

His tes - ti - mo - ny is most sure, Pro - claim - ing wis - dom's way.

Fear and Faith

Psalm 56
Uzziah C. Burnap

Psalter #152

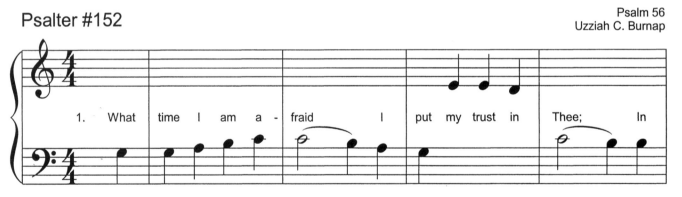

1. What time I am a - fraid I put my trust in Thee; In

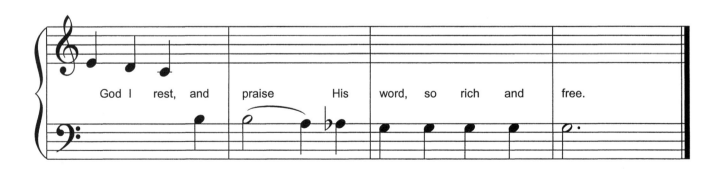

God I rest, and praise His word, so rich and free.

As the Hart, About to Falter

Psalter #416

Psalm 42
L. Bourgeois, 1551

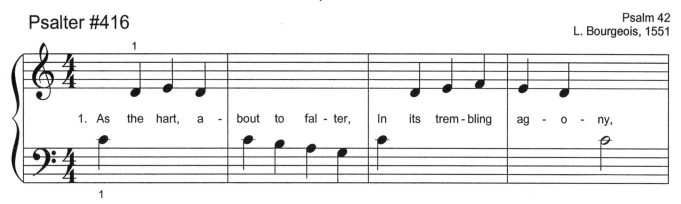

1. As the hart, a - bout to fal - ter, In its trem - bling ag - o - ny,

Pant - eth for the brooks of wa - ter, So my soul doth pant for Thee.

Yea, a - thirst for Thee I cry; God of life, O when shall I

Come a - gain to stand be - fore Thee In Thy tem - ple, and a - dore Thee?

A Prayer of Faith

Psalm 71
Hugh Wilson

Psalter #192

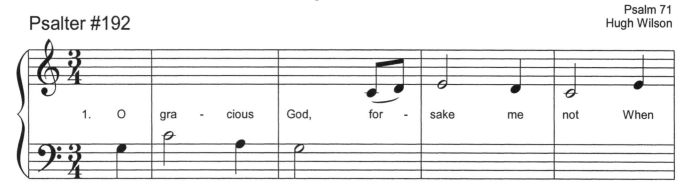

1. O gra - cious God, for - sake me not When

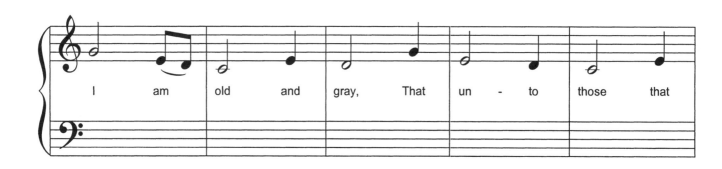

I am old and gray, That un - to those that

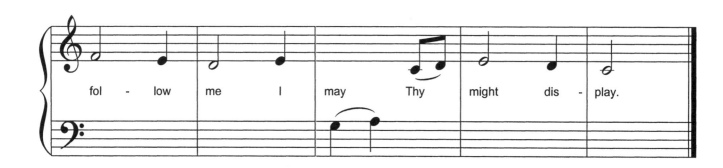

fol - low me I may Thy might dis - play.

The Witness of Nature to God

Psalm 19
John B. Herbert

Psalter #39

1. The heav'ns in their splen - dor de - clare The might and the glo - ry of

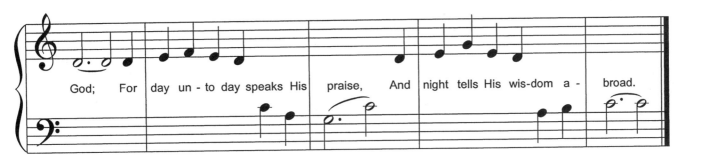

God; For day un-to day speaks His praise, And night tells His wis-dom a - broad.

Personal Devotion to God

Psalm 40
William Gardiner

Psalter #109

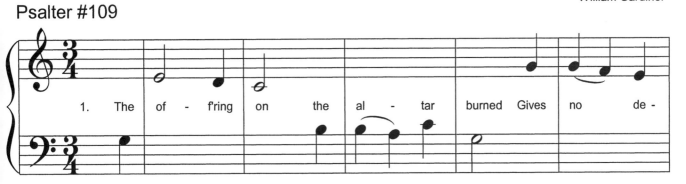

1. The of - f'ring on the al - tar burned Gives no de -

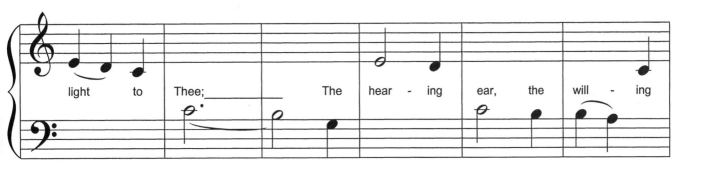

light to Thee;_____ The hear - ing ear, the will - ing

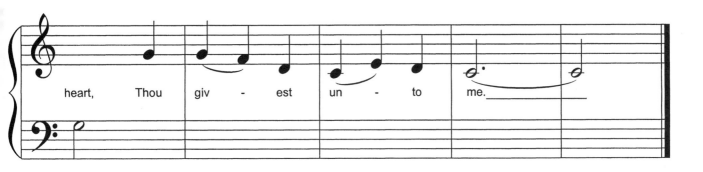

heart, Thou giv - est un - to me._____

The Righteous and Unrighteous

Psalm 1
Luther O. Emerson

Psalter #2

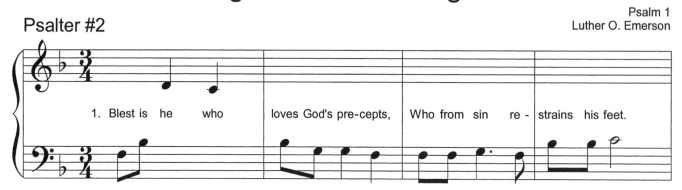

1. Blest is he who loves God's pre-cepts, Who from sin re - strains his feet.

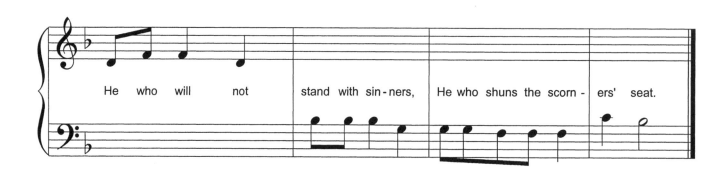

He who will not stand with sin - ners, He who shuns the scorn - ers' seat.

Trustful Praise and Prayer

Psalm 144
A. Browns

Psalter #392

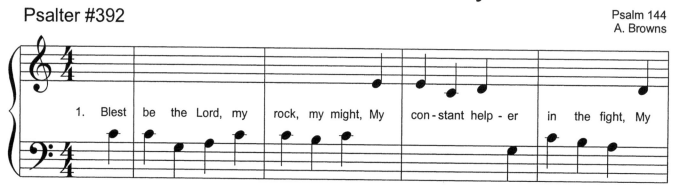

1. Blest be the Lord, my rock, my might, My con - stant help - er in the fight, My

shield, my right - eous - ness, My strong high tower, my Sav - iour true, Who

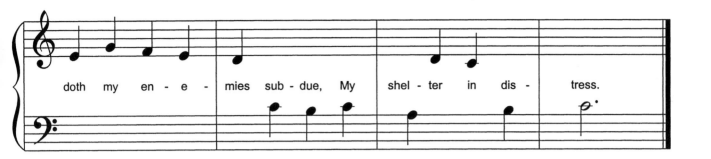

doth my en-e-mies sub-due, My shel-ter in dis-tress.

Reminders from Israel's History

Psalter #214

Psalm 78
Crown of Jesus Music

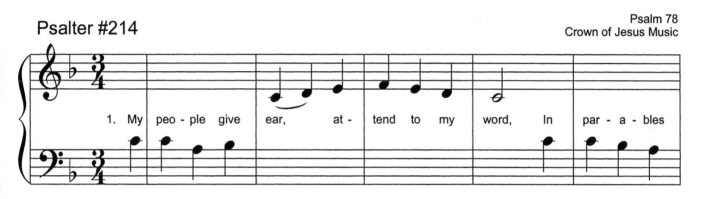

1. My peo-ple give ear, at-tend to my word, In par-a-bles

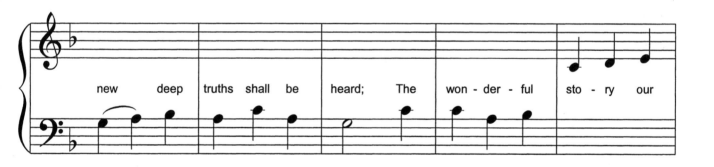

new deep truths shall be heard; The won-der-ful sto-ry our

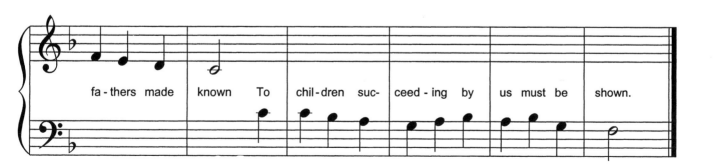

fa-thers made known To chil-dren suc-ceed-ing by us must be shown.

A Vindication of God's Ways

Psalm 73
Welsh Melody

Psalter #201 - second tune

1. God lov - eth the right-eous, His good-ness is sure, He nev - er for-

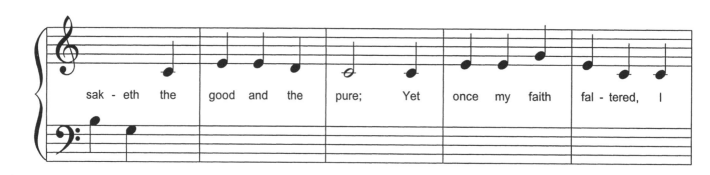

sak - eth the good and the pure; Yet once my faith fal - tered, I

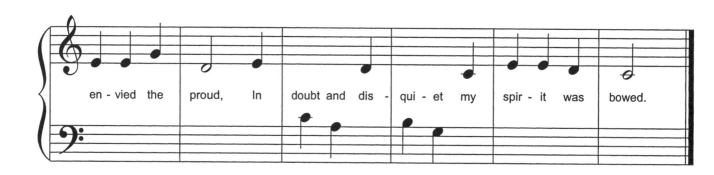

en - vied the proud, In doubt and dis - qui - et my spir - it was bowed.

Abiding Confidence and Hope

Psalm 71
Isaac B. Woodbury

Psalter #191

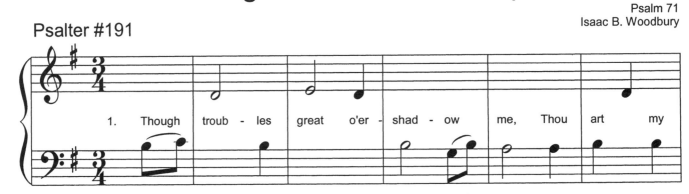

1. Though troub - les great o'er - shad - ow me, Thou art my

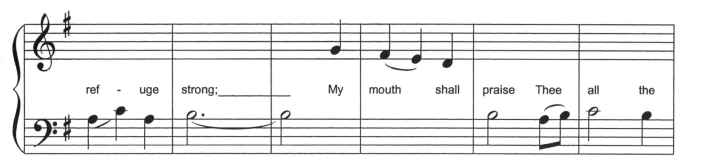

ref - uge strong;_____ My mouth shall praise Thee all the

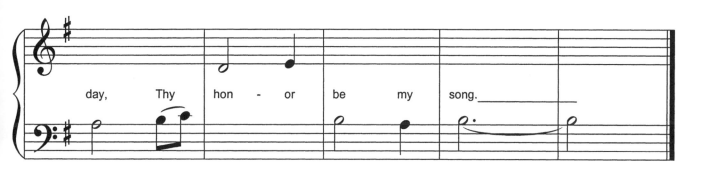

day, Thy hon - or be my song._____

Benediction upon the God-Fearing

Psalter #309

Psalm 115
William Croft

1. The Lord Who has re - mem-bered us His bless-ing will be - stow; All

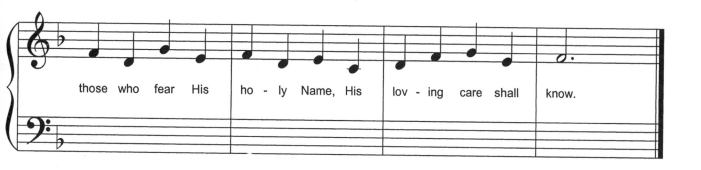

those who fear His ho - ly Name, His lov - ing care shall know.

Days in the Sanctuary

Psalm 84
Joseph Barnby

Psalter #229

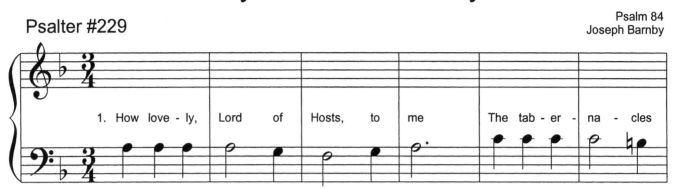

1. How love - ly, Lord of Hosts, to me The tab - er - na - cles

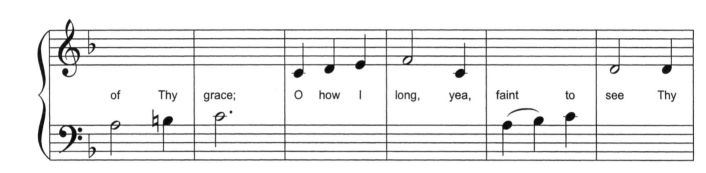

of Thy grace; O how I long, yea, faint to see Thy

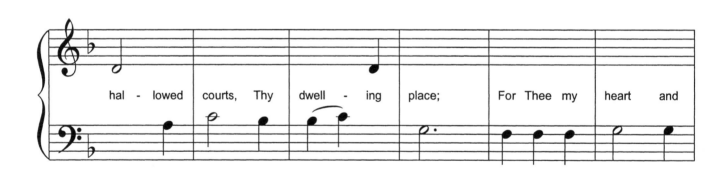

hal - lowed courts, Thy dwell - ing place; For Thee my heart and

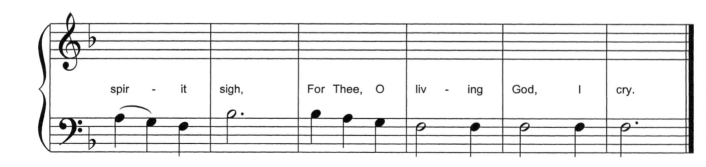

spir - it sigh, For Thee, O liv - ing God, I cry.

The Universal King

Psalm 96
Lowell Mason

Psalter #259

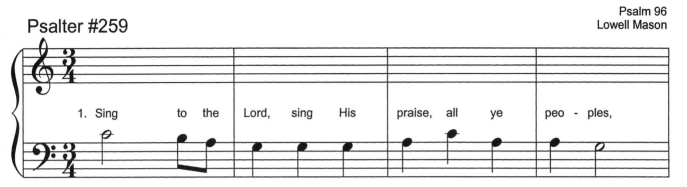

1. Sing to the Lord, sing His praise, all ye peo - ples,

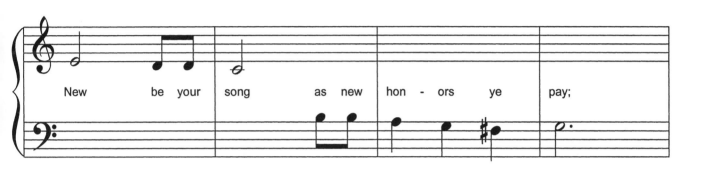

New be your song as new hon - ors ye pay;

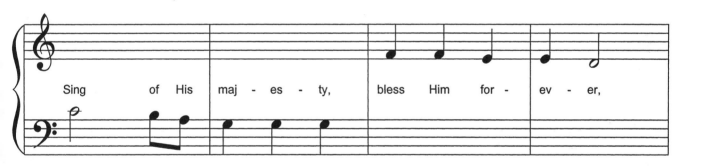

Sing of His maj - es - ty, bless Him for - ev - er,

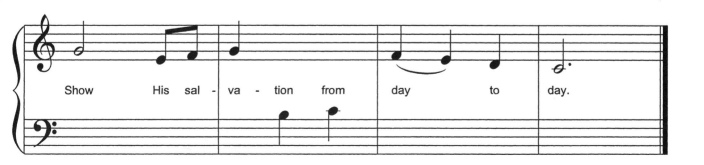

Show His sal - va - tion from day to day.

Redemption and Grateful Love

Psalm 116
Arranged from Schumann

Psalter #310

1. I love the Lord, for my re - quest And hum - ble plea He makes His care; In

Him through life my faith shall rest, For He both hears and an - swers prayer.

Assurance of Blessing

Psalm 85
Arranged by Edward Miller

Psalter #230

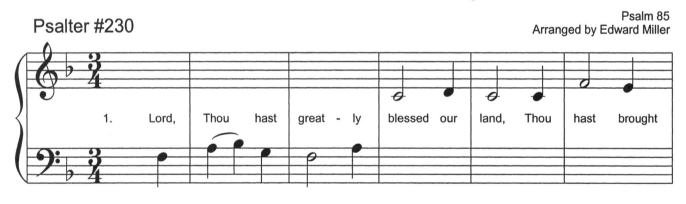

1. Lord, Thou hast great - ly blessed our land, Thou hast brought

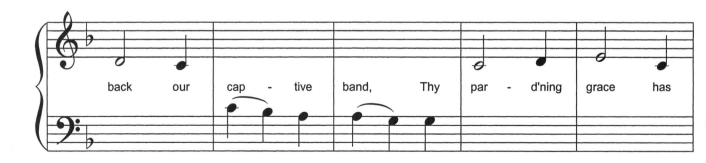

back our cap - tive band, Thy par - d'ning grace has

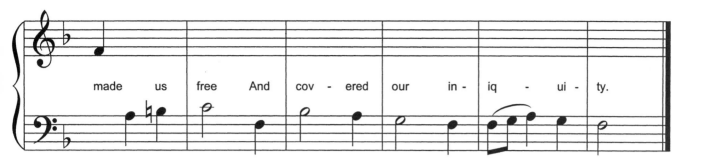

made us free And cov - ered our in - iq - ui - ty.

The Wondrous Testimonies of God

Psalter #337

Psalm 119
Thomas B. Southgate

1. Thy won - drous tes - ti - mo - nies, Lord, My soul will

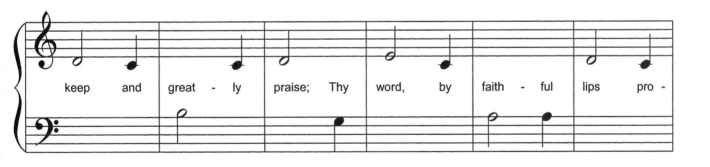

keep and great - ly praise; Thy word, by faith - ful lips pro -

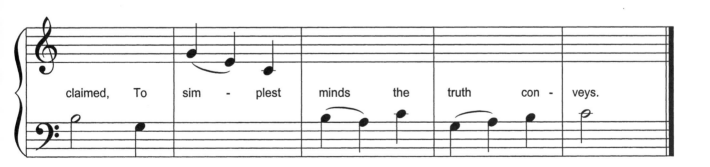

claimed, To sim - plest minds the truth con - veys.

Aspects of the Divine Character

Psalter #208

Psalm 76
Arranged from Mozart

1. A - mong His peo - ple God is known, Most glo - rious in His

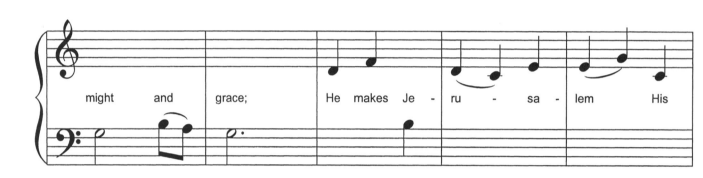

might and grace; He makes Je - ru - sa - lem His

throne, Her peace - ful hills His dwell - ing - place.

The Hallelujah Chorus

Psalter #413

Psalm 150
Sicilian Melody

1. Hal - le - lu - jah! Hal - le - lu - jah! Earth and heav'n in sweet ac - cord

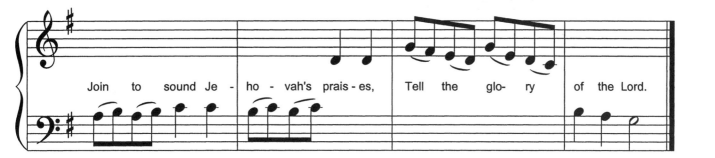

Join to sound Je - ho - vah's prais - es, Tell the glo- ry of the Lord.

Universal Praise

Psalm 100
George C. Stebbins

Psalter #269

1. All peo - ple that dwell on the earth,_____ Your songs to Je -

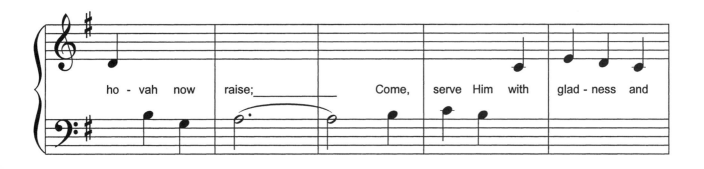

ho - vah now raise;_____ Come, serve Him with glad - ness and

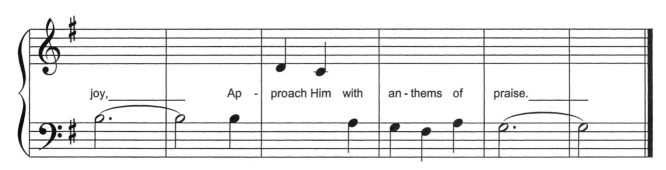

joy,_____ Ap - proach Him with an - thems of praise._____

Unto the Lord Lift Thankful Voices

Psalter #425

Psalm 105
Maitre Pierre, 1562

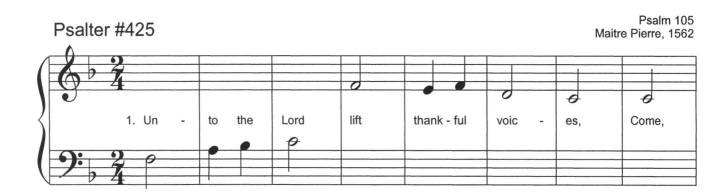

1. Un - to the Lord lift thank - ful voic - es, Come,

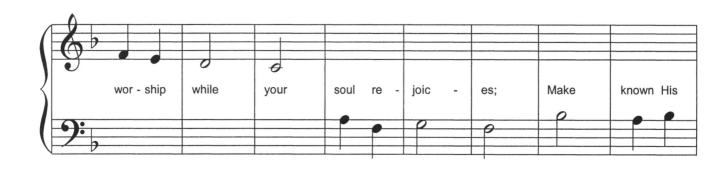

wor - ship while your soul re - joic - es; Make known His

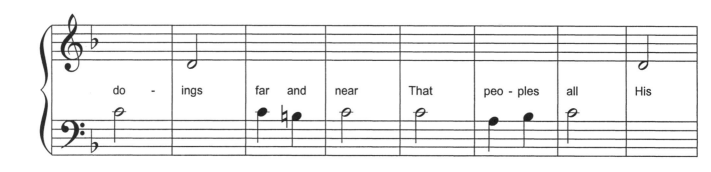

do - ings far and near That peo - ples all His

Name may fear, And tell, in man - y joy - ful

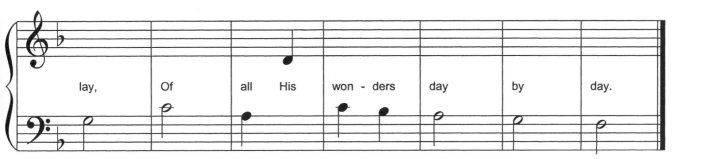

lay, Of all His won - ders day by day.

The Greatness of God in Nature

Psalter #285

Psalm 104
Arranged from Michael Haydn

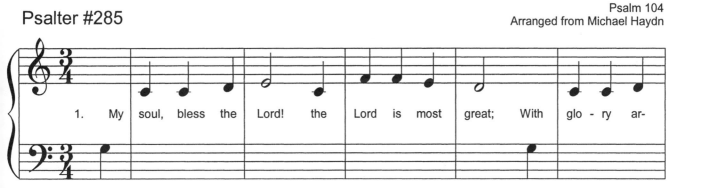

1. My soul, bless the Lord! the Lord is most great; With glo - ry ar-

rayed, ma - jes - tic His state; The light is His gar - ment, the

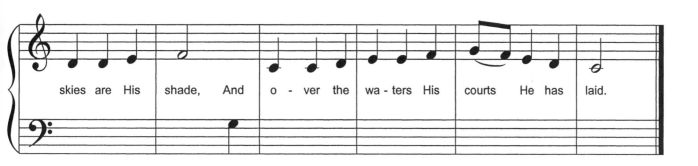

skies are His shade, And o - ver the wa - ters His courts He has laid.

The Confidence of Faith

Psalm 27
Albert L. Peace

Psalter #73

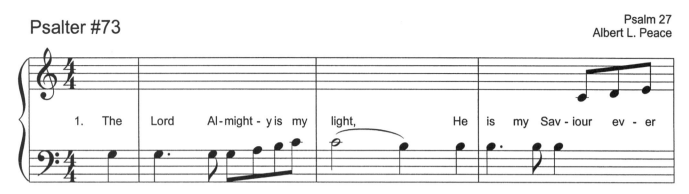

1. The Lord Al-might-y is my light, He is my Sav-iour ev-er

near, And, since my strength is in His might Who

can dis-tress me or af-fright? What e-vil shall I fear?

The Petition of a Good Conscience

Psalm 26
English Melody

Psalter #69

1. Be Thou my judge, O right-eous Lord, Try Thou my in-most heart;

I walk with stead - fast trust in Thee, Nor from Thy ways de - part.

Commemoration and Praise

Psalm 30
Greek Melody

Psalter #77

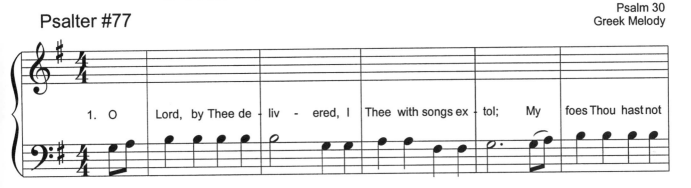

1. O Lord, by Thee de - liv - ered, I Thee with songs ex - tol; My foes Thou hast not

suf - fered To glo - ry o'er my fall. O Lord, my God, I sought Thee, And Thou didst heal and

save; Thou, Lord, from death didst ran - som And keep me from the grave.

Satisfaction in God

Psalter #163

Psalm 63
George C. Stebbins

1. O Lord, my God, most ear - nest - ly My heart would seek Thy face, With -

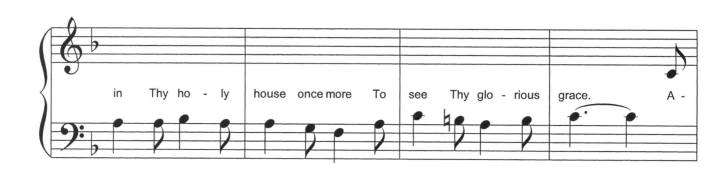

in Thy ho - ly house once more To see Thy glo - rious grace. A -

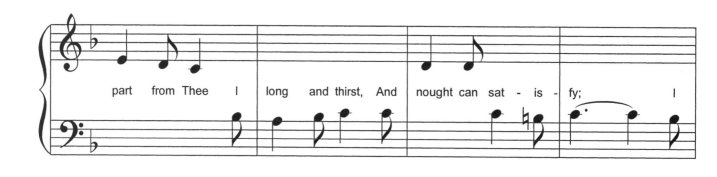

part from Thee I long and thirst, And nought can sat - is - fy; I

wan - der in a des - ert land Where all the streams are dry.

The Frailty of Life

Psalter #104

Psalm 39
John E. Gould

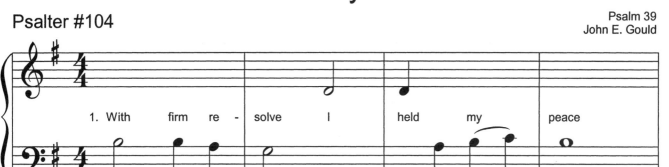

1. With firm re - solve I held my peace

And spake not ei - ther bad or good.

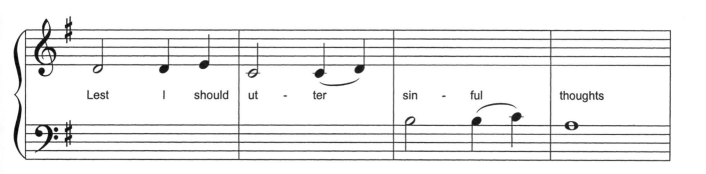

Lest I should ut - ter sin - ful thoughts

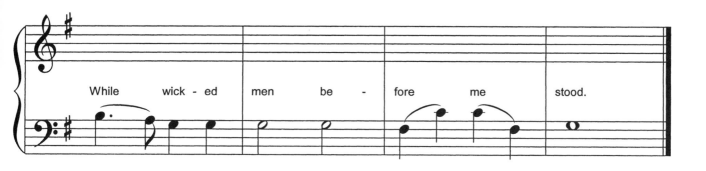

While wick - ed men be - fore me stood.

Penitential Prayers

Psalter #140

Psalm 51
Richard Redhead

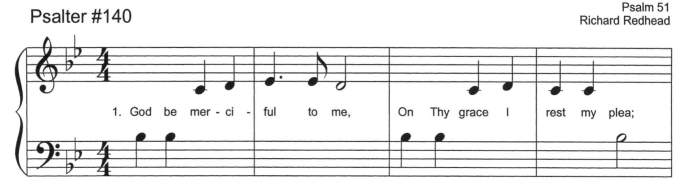

1. God be mer - ci - ful to me, On Thy grace I rest my plea;

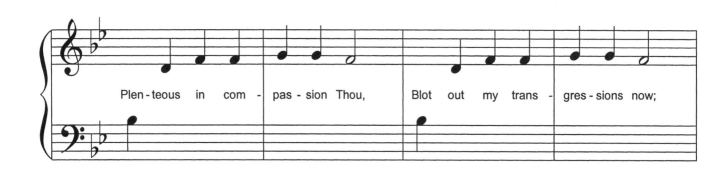

Plen - teous in com - pas - sion Thou, Blot out my trans - gres - sions now;

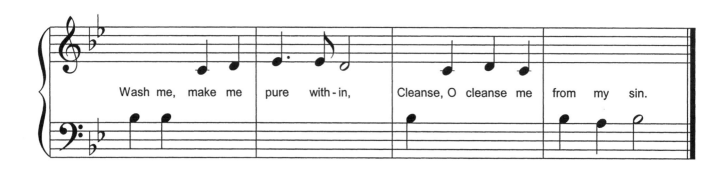

Wash me, make me pure with - in, Cleanse, O cleanse me from my sin.

A Faithful Creator

Psalter #286

Psalm 104
John Stanley

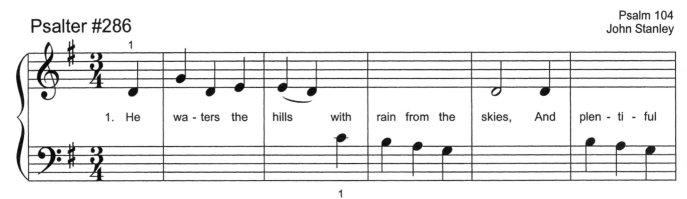

1. He wa - ters the hills with rain from the skies, And plen - ti - ful

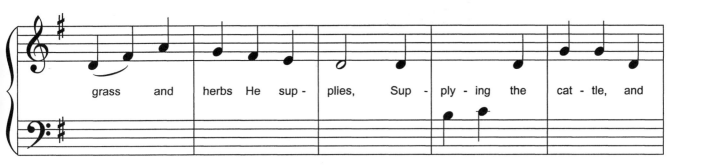

grass and herbs He sup - plies, Sup - ply - ing the cat - tle, and

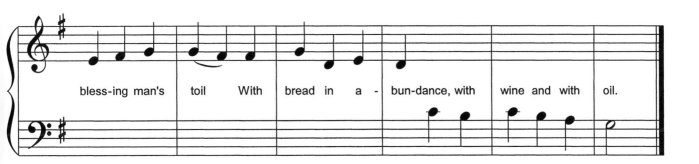

bless-ing man's toil With bread in a - bun-dance, with wine and with oil.

A Plea for Salvation

Psalter #103

Psalm 38
Lowell Mason

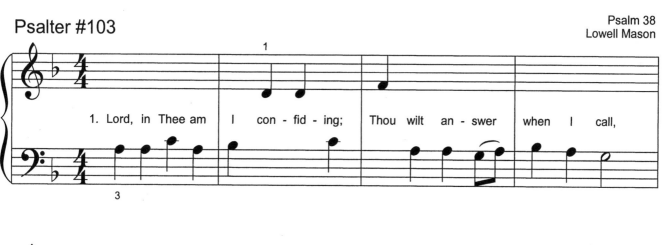

1. Lord, in Thee am I con - fid - ing; Thou wilt an - swer when I call,

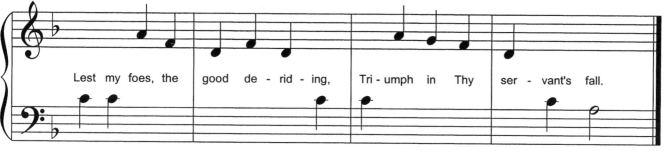

Lest my foes, the good de - rid - ing, Tri - umph in Thy ser - vant's fall.

Longing after God

Psalm 42
Arranged from Joseph Barnby

Psalter #115

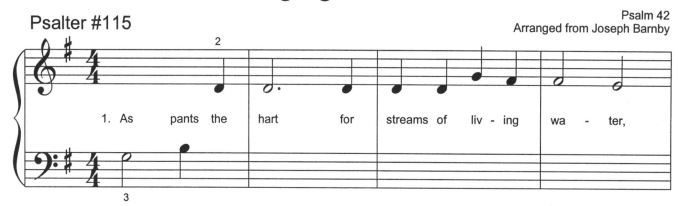

1. As pants the hart for streams of liv-ing wa-ter,

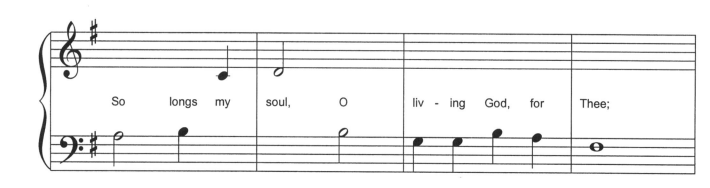

So longs my soul, O liv-ing God, for Thee;

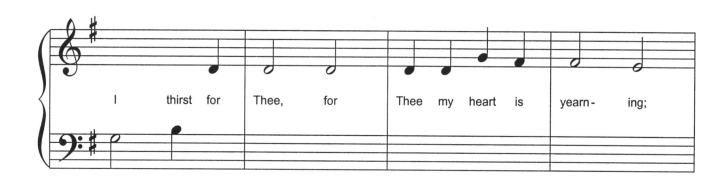

I thirst for Thee, for Thee my heart is yearn-ing;

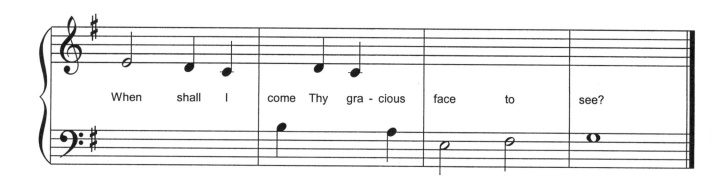

When shall I come Thy gra-cious face to see?

The Mercies and Faithfulness of God

Psalm 89
H. Percy Smith

Psalter #241

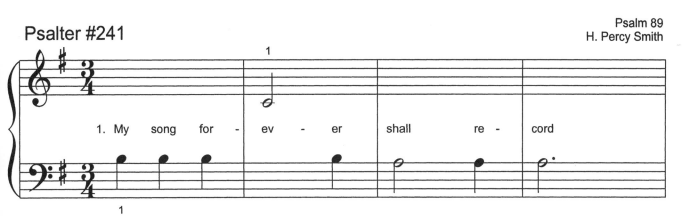

1. My song for - ev - er shall re - cord

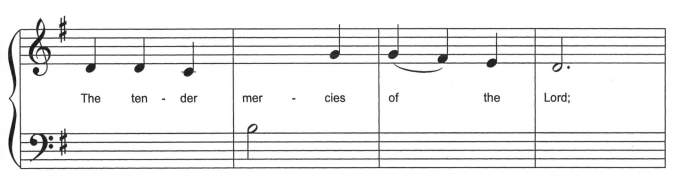

The ten - der mer - cies of the Lord;

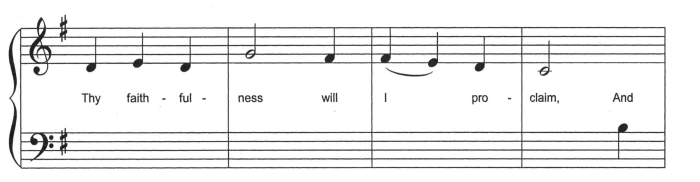

Thy faith - ful - ness will I pro - claim, And

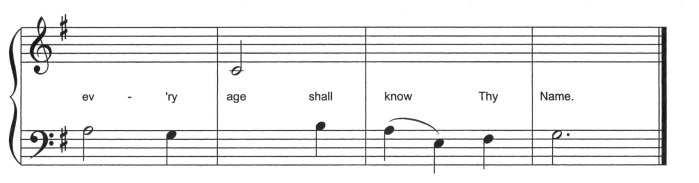

ev - 'ry age shall know Thy Name.

Motives to Gratitude

Psalm 103
James Walch

Psalter #283

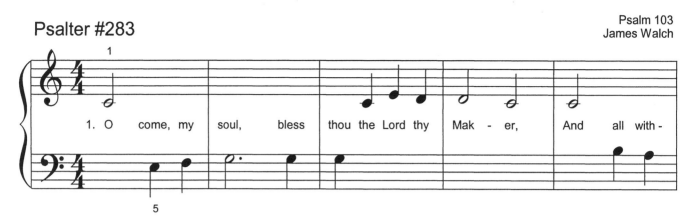

1. O come, my soul, bless thou the Lord thy Mak - er, And all with -

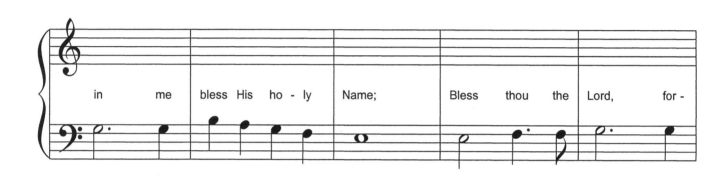

in me bless His ho - ly Name; Bless thou the Lord, for -

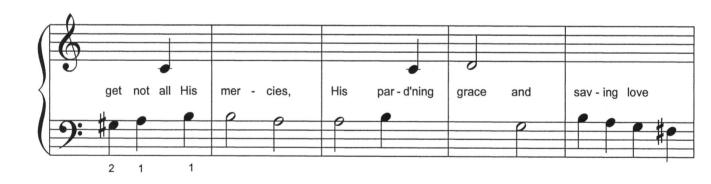

get not all His mer - cies, His par - d'ning grace and sav - ing love

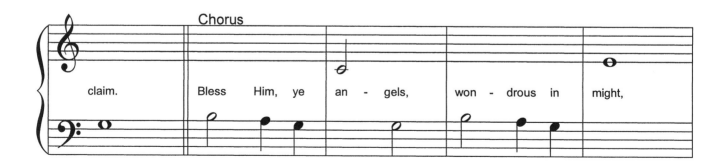

Chorus

claim. Bless Him, ye an - gels, won - drous in might,

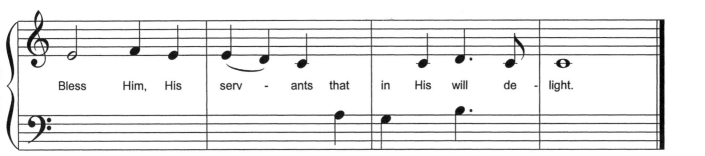

Bless Him, His serv - ants that in His will de - light.

The Blessed and Only Potentate

Psalter #282

Psalm 103
Ithamar Conkey

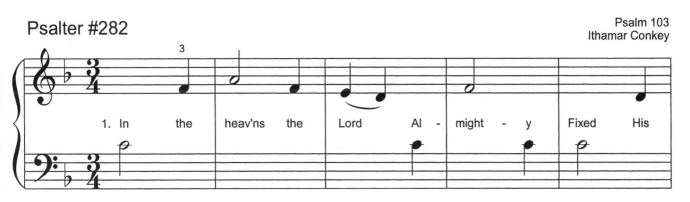

1. In the heav'ns the Lord Al - might - y Fixed His

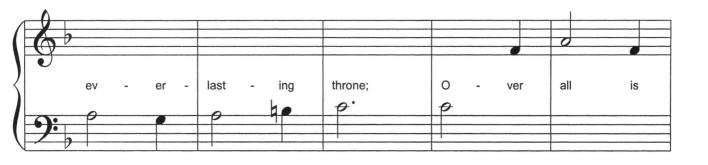

ev - er - last - ing throne; O - ver all is

His do - min - ion, He is God, and He a - lone.

A Revived Church and Missions

Psalter #176

Psalm 67
Samuel S. Wesley

1. O God, to us show mer - cy And bless us in Thy grace; Cause Thou to shine up-

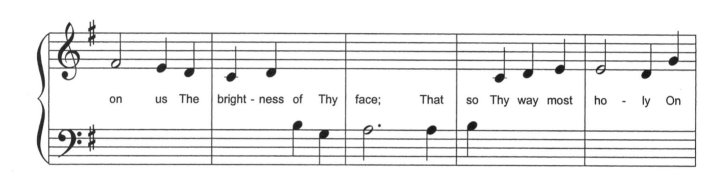

on us The bright - ness of Thy face; That so Thy way most ho - ly On

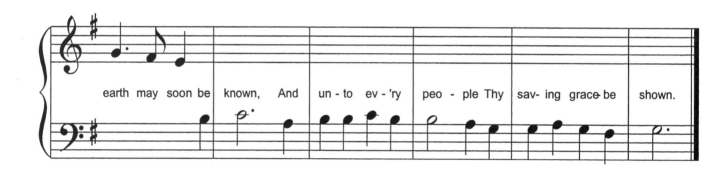

earth may soon be known, And un - to ev - 'ry peo - ple Thy sav - ing grace be shown.

Emancipation from Spiritual Slavery

Psalm 107
Arranged from Conrad Kocher

Psalter #293

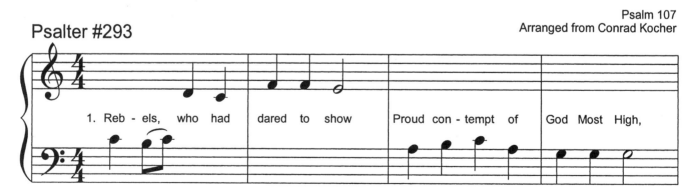

1. Reb - els, who had dared to show Proud con - tempt of God Most High,

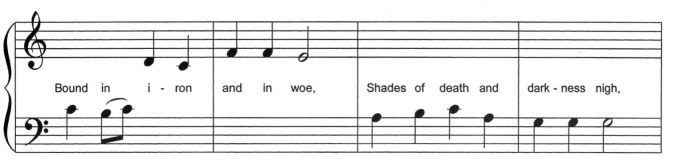

Bound in i-ron and in woe, Shades of death and dark-ness nigh,

Hum-bled low with toil and pain, Fell, and looked for help in vain.

Incentives to Praise

Psalm 135
A. Croil Falconer

Psalter #373

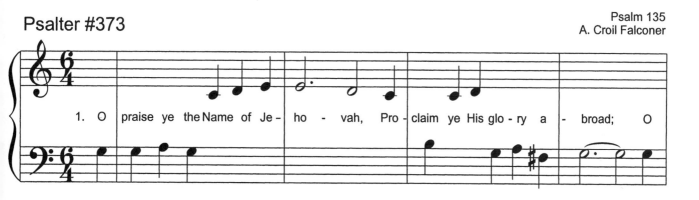

1. O praise ye the Name of Je-ho-vah, Pro-claim ye His glo-ry a-broad; O

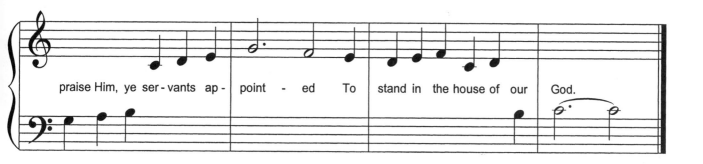

praise Him, ye ser-vants ap-point-ed To stand in the house of our God.

Divine Deliverance

Psalter #353

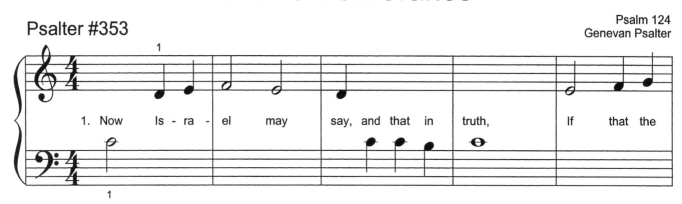

1. Now Is - ra - el may say, and that in truth, If that the

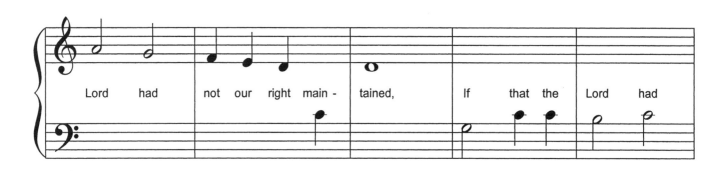

Lord had not our right main - tained, If that the Lord had

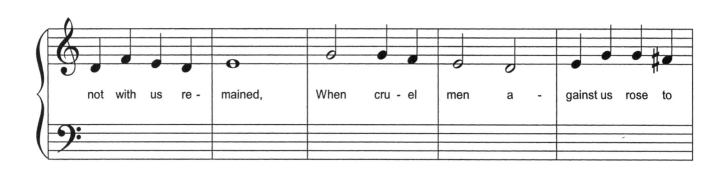

not with us re - mained, When cru - el men a - gainst us rose to

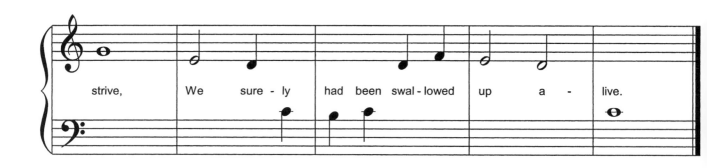

strive, We sure - ly had been swal - lowed up a - live.

The Universal Fellowship of Worship

Psalter #315

Psalm 117
George C. Stebbins

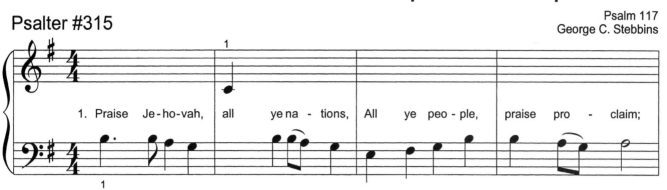

1. Praise Je-ho-vah, all ye na - tions, All ye peo - ple, praise pro - claim;

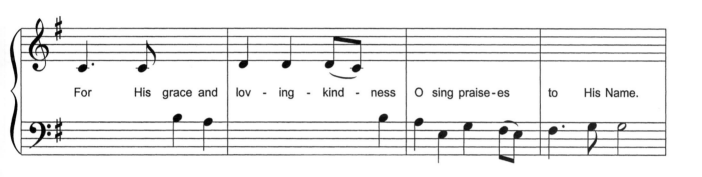

For His grace and lov - ing - kind - ness O sing praise-es to His Name.

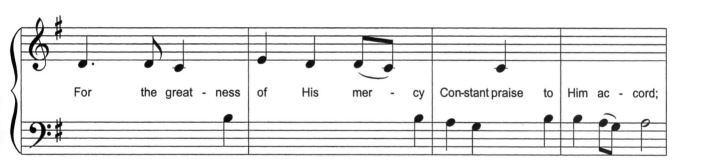

For the great - ness of His mer - cy Con-stant praise to Him ac - cord;

Ev - er-more His truth en - dur - eth; Hal - le-lu-jah, praise the Lord.

Supplication and Testimony

Psalm 69
William H. Monk

Psalter #187

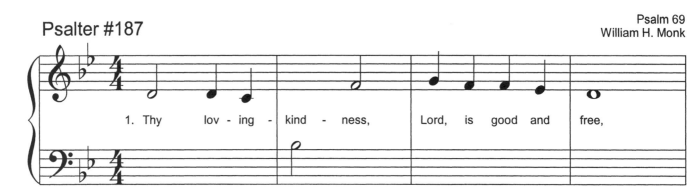

1. Thy lov - ing - kind - ness, Lord, is good and free,

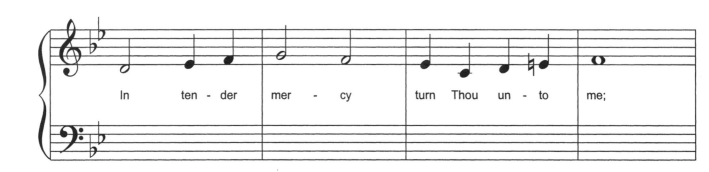

In ten - der mer - cy turn Thou un - to me;

Hide not Thy face from me in my dis - tress,

In mer - cy hear my prayer, Thy serv - ant bless.

Adoration and Submission

Psalter #255

Psalm 95
John Zundel

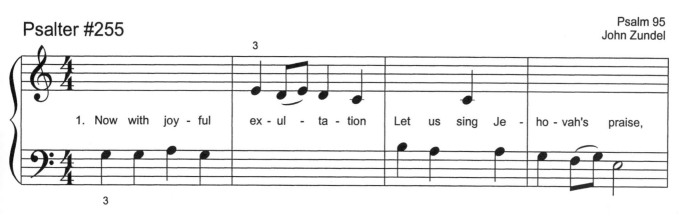

1. Now with joy - ful ex - ul - ta - tion Let us sing Je - ho - vah's praise,

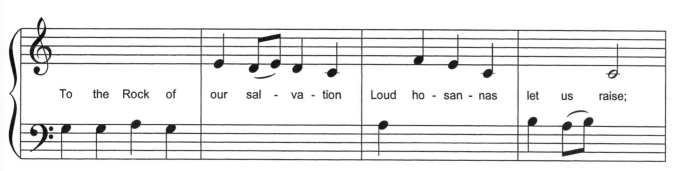

To the Rock of our sal - va - tion Loud ho - san - nas let us raise;

Thank - ful trib - ute glad - ly bring - ing, Let us come be - fore Him now,

And, with psalms His prais - es sing - ing, Joy - ful in His pres - ence bow.

The Holiness of God

Psalm 99
John B. Dykes

Psalter #266

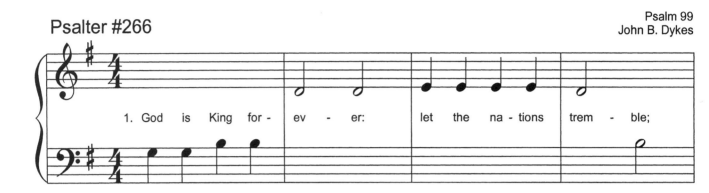

1. God is King for - ev - er: let the na - tions trem - ble;

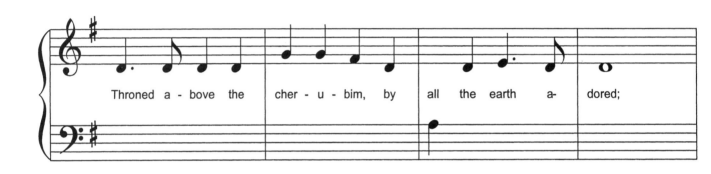

Throned a - bove the cher - u - bim, by all the earth a - dored;

He is great in Zi - on, high a - bove all peo - ples;

Praise Him with fear, for ho - ly is the Lord.

Conscious Dependence on God

Psalter #359

Psalm 127
Joseph E. Sweetser

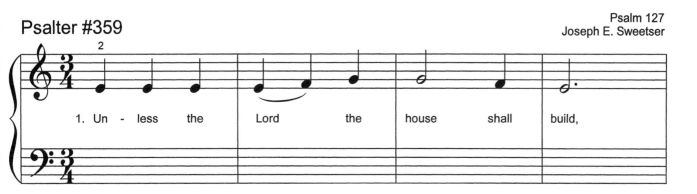

1. Un - less the Lord the house shall build,

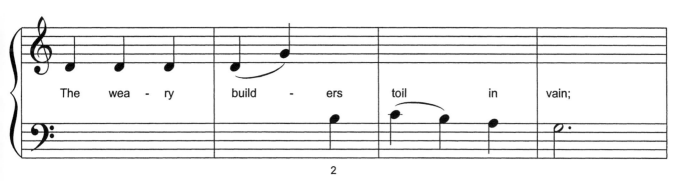

The wea - ry build - ers toil in vain;

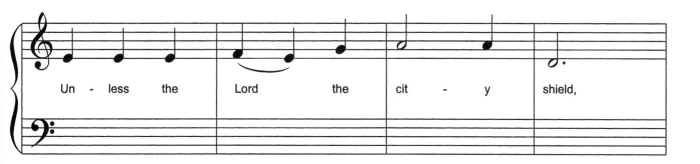

Un - less the Lord the cit - y shield,

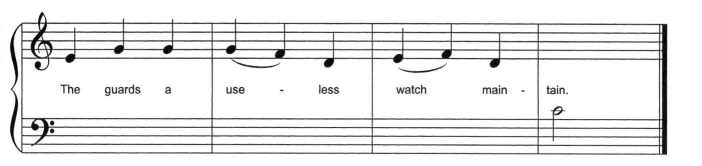

The guards a use - less watch main - tain.

Guidance for Youth

Psalm 119
William H. Doane

Psalter #322

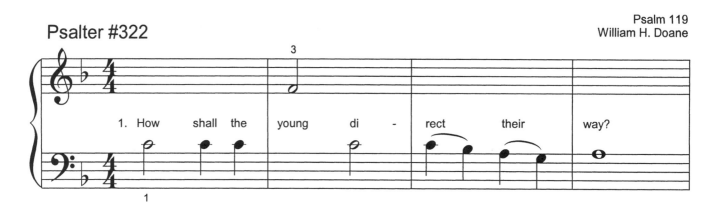

1. How shall the young di - rect their way?

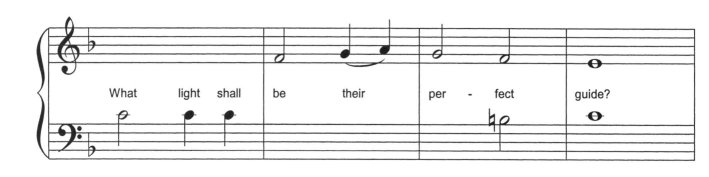

What light shall be their per - fect guide?

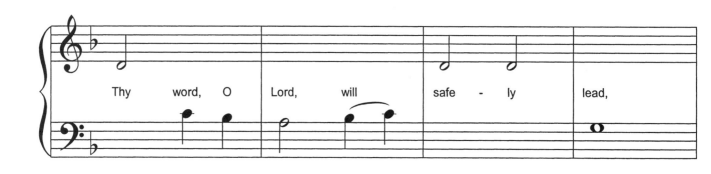

Thy word, O Lord, will safe - ly lead,

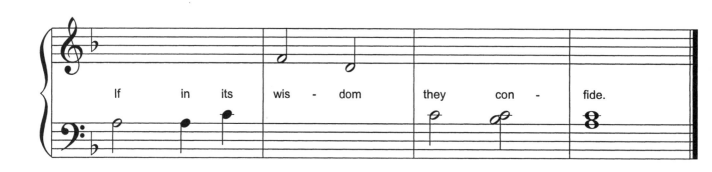

If in its wis - dom they con - fide.

Reasons for Praise

Psalm 147
John B. Dykes

Psalter #402

1. O sing ye Hal-le-lu - jah! 'Tis good our God to praise; 'Tis

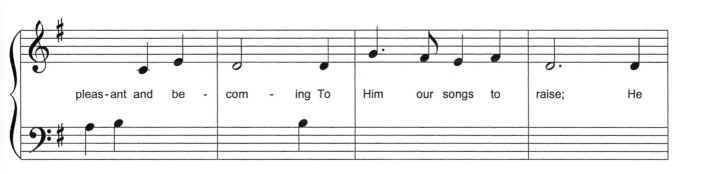

pleas-ant and be - com - ing To Him our songs to raise; He

builds the walls of Zi - on, He seeks her wan - d'ring sons, He

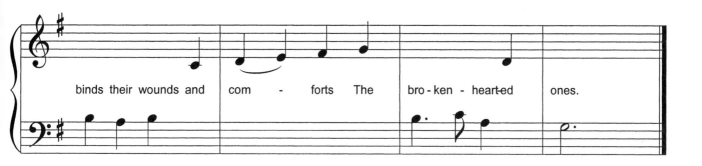

binds their wounds and com - forts The bro-ken - heart-ed ones.

Contrite Trust

Psalm 143
Frederick C. Maker

Psalter #389

1. Lord, hear me in dis - tress, Re - gard my sup - pliant cry,

And in Thy faith - ful - ness And right - eous - ness re - ply.

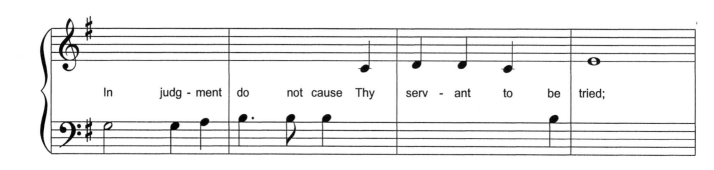

In judg - ment do not cause Thy serv - ant to be tried;

Be - fore Thy ho - ly laws No man is jus - ti - fied.

Longings for Sanctuary Fellowship

Psalm 84
Arthur S. Sullivan

Psalter #226

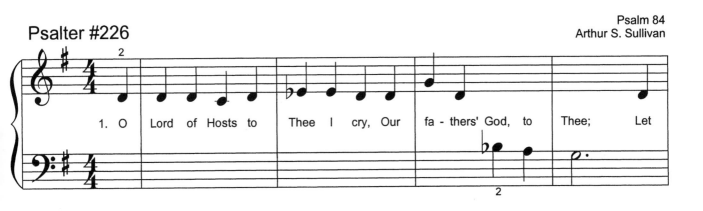

1. O Lord of Hosts to Thee I cry, Our fa - thers' God, to Thee; Let

my pe - ti - tion reach Thy ear, My prayer ac - cept - ed be; O

God our shield, look Thou on us, Re - veal Thy - self in grace, And

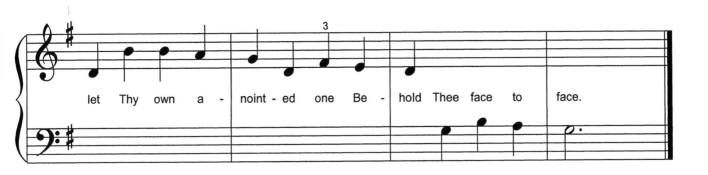

let Thy own a - noint - ed one Be - hold Thee face to face.

Covenant Faithfulness

Psalter #243

Psalm 89
William Tans'ur

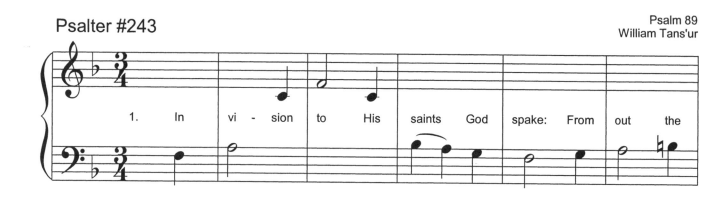

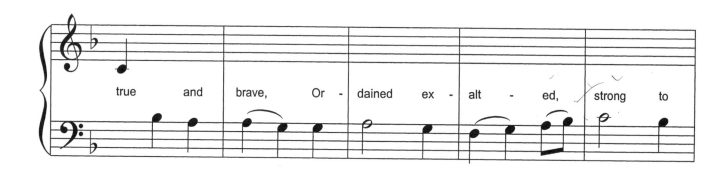

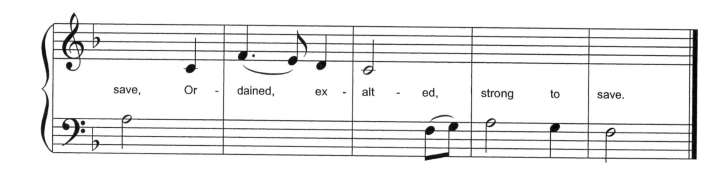

A Vindication of God's Ways

Psalter #201

Psalm 73
John P. Campbell

1. God lov - eth the right - eous, His good - ness is sure, He

nev - er for - sak - eth the good and the pure; Yet

once my faith fal - tered, I en - vied the proud, In

doubt and dis - qui - et my spir - it was bowed.

Exultant Praise

Psalter #406

Psalm 149
Arranged from Handel

1. Praise ye the Lord a - mong His saints, New songs of glad - ness sing; Let Zi - on's chil - dren praise and bless Their Mak - er and their King, Their Mak - er and their King.

Expectancy of Grace

Psalter #232

Psalm 85
John B. Dykes

1. O Lord, to us Thy mer - cy show, And Thy sal - va - tion now be - stow; We

wait to hear what God will say; Peace to His peo - ple He will speak, And

to His saints, but let them seek No more in fol - ly's path to stray.

The Creator Glorified

Psalm 104
William J. Kirkpatrick

Psalter #288

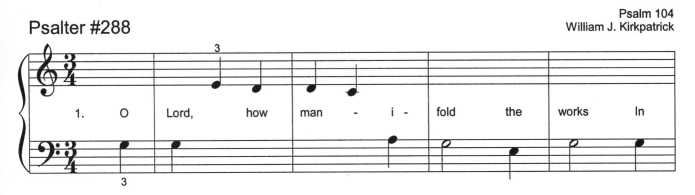

1. O Lord, how man - i - fold the works In

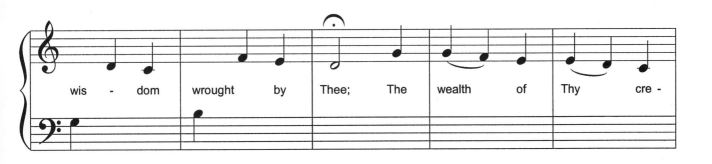

wis - dom wrought by Thee; The wealth of Thy cre -

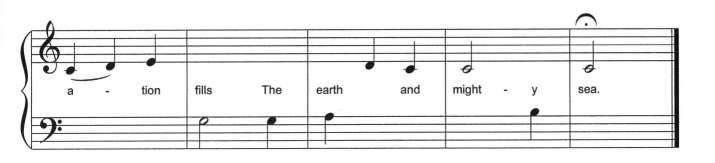

a - tion fills The earth and might - y sea.

The Divine Goodness

Psalm 119
Charles H. Gabriel

1. Thou, Lord, hast dealt well with Thy ser - vant, Thy prom - ise is

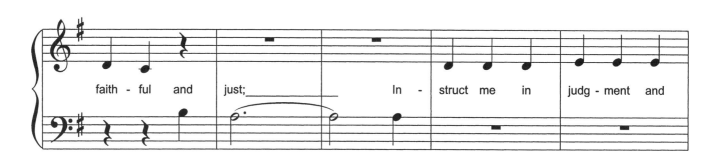

faith - ful and just; In - struct me in judg - ment and

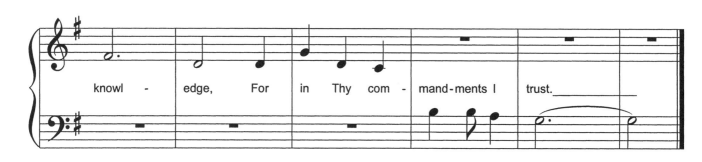

knowl - edge, For in Thy com - mand-ments I trust.

Worship and Its Motives

Psalm 95
Isaac B. Woodbury

1. O come and to Je - ho - vah sing, To Him our voi - ces

raise; Let us in our most joy - ful songs The Lord our

Sav - iour praise, The Lord our Sav - iour praise.

The World-Wide Praise of God

Psalm 117
Johann G. Braun

Psalter #316

1. All men on earth that live, To God all glo - ry give, Praise ye the

Lord; His lov - ing - kind - ness bless, His con - stant faith - ful - ness

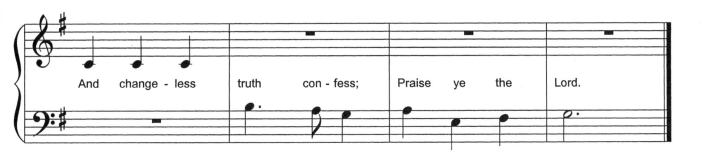

And change - less truth con - fess; Praise ye the Lord.

Devotion to the Church

Psalm 122
Lowell Mason

Psalter #350

1. With joy I heard my friends ex - claim,

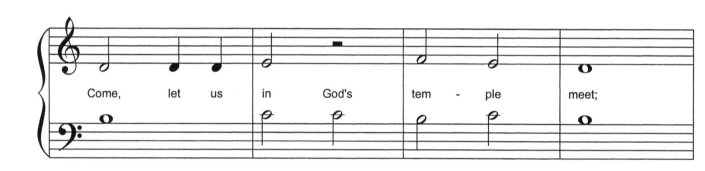

Come, let us in God's tem - ple meet;

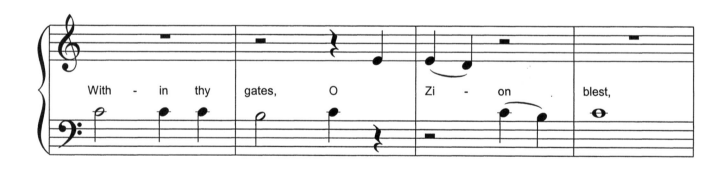

With - in thy gates, O Zi - on blest,

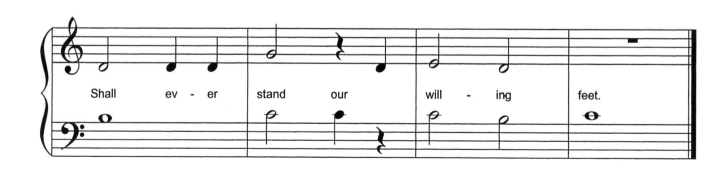

Shall ev - er stand our will - ing feet.

The False Tongue

Psalm 120
Thomas Hastings

Psalter #343

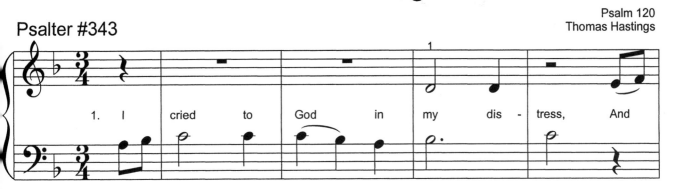

1. I cried to God in my dis - tress, And

by the Lord my prayer was heard; O save me,

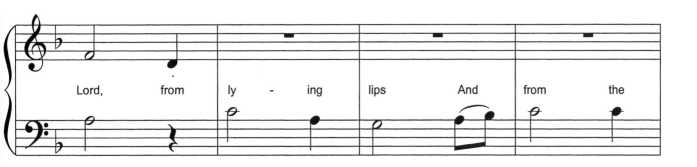

Lord, from ly - ing lips And from the

false, de - ceit - ful word.

Praise and Trust

Psalter #134

Psalm 48
George J. Elvey

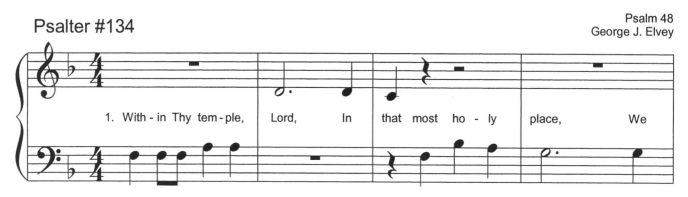

1. With - in Thy tem - ple, Lord, In that most ho - ly place, We

on Thy lov - ing - kind - ness dwell, The won - ders of Thy grace. Men

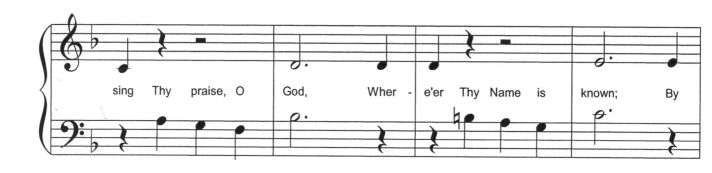

sing Thy praise, O God, Wher - e'er Thy Name is known; By

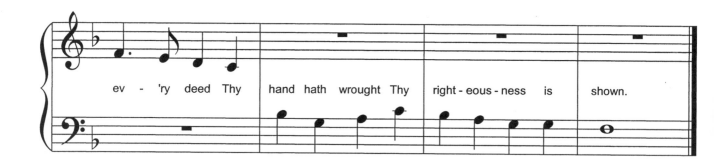

ev - 'ry deed Thy hand hath wrought Thy right - eous - ness is shown.

Gratitude and Confidence

Psalter #298

Psalm 108
William F. Sherwin

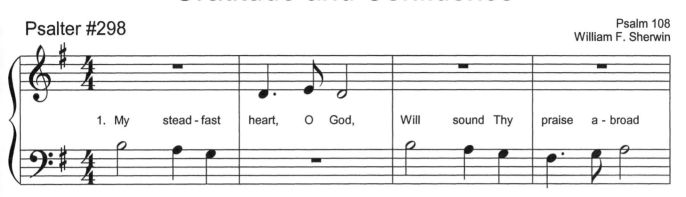

1. My stead-fast heart, O God, Will sound Thy praise a-broad

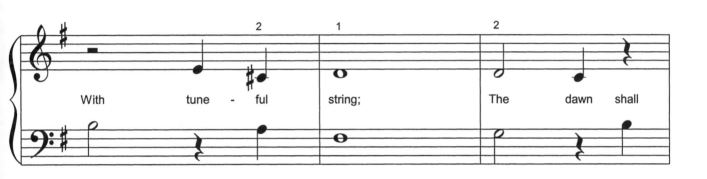

With tune-ful string; The dawn shall

hear my song, Thy praise I will pro-long, And where Thy

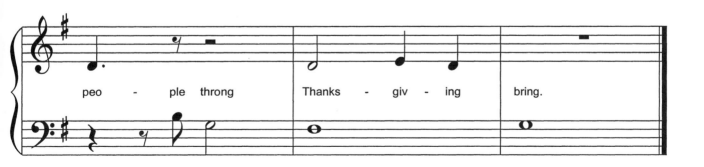

peo - ple throng Thanks - giv - ing bring.

A Suppliant's Urgent Prayer

Psalm 70
Hart P. Danks

Psalter #188

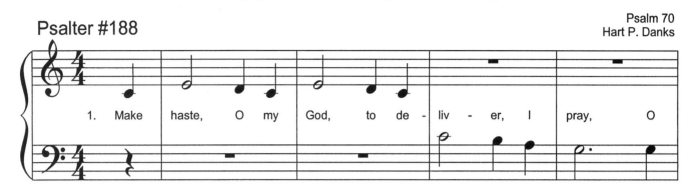

1. Make haste, O my God, to de - liv - er, I pray, O

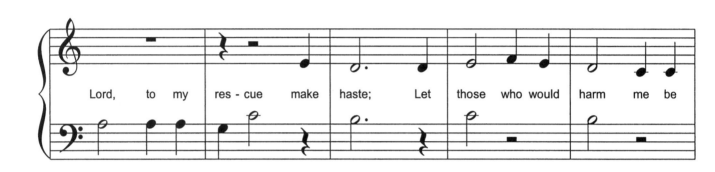

Lord, to my res - cue make haste; Let those who would harm me be

filled with dis - may, And in their own fol - ly dis - graced.

Reliance and Supplication

Psalm 143
Arthur J. Jamouneau

Psalter #391

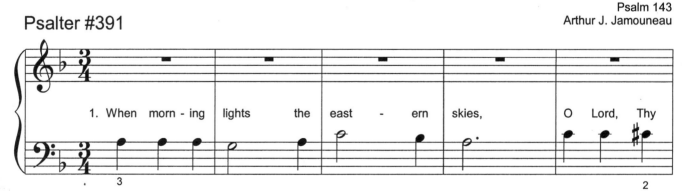

1. When morn - ing lights the east - ern skies, O Lord, Thy

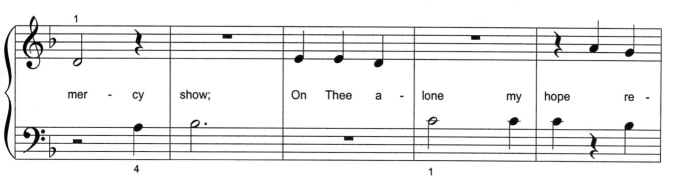

mer - cy show; On Thee a - lone my hope re-

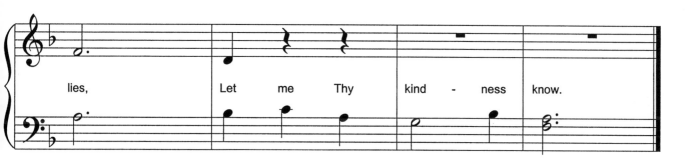

lies, Let me Thy kind - ness know.

Trustful Entreaty and Praise

Psalm 71
Anonymous

Psalter #190

1. In Thee, O Lord, I put my trust; Shamed let me nev-er be; O save me in Thy

right-eous-ness, Give ear, and res-cue me, Give ear, and res-cue me.

Prayer for Restoring Grace

Psalter #220

Psalm 80
Ira D. Sankey

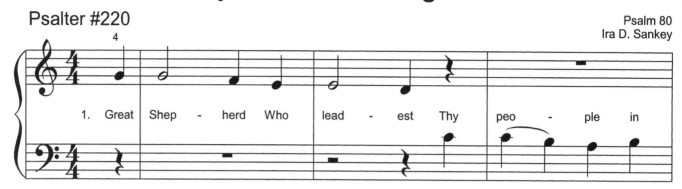

1. Great Shep - herd Who lead - est Thy peo - ple in

love, 'Mid cher - u - bim dwell - ing, shine Thou from a -

bove; In might come and save us, Thy peo - ple re - store, And

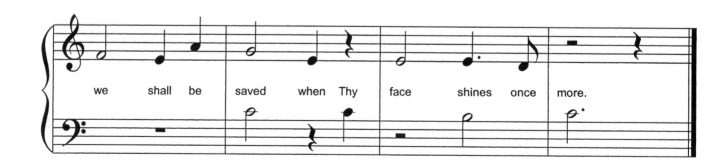

we shall be saved when Thy face shines once more.

Triumphant Joy in God

Psalm 149
Felice Giardini

Psalter #408

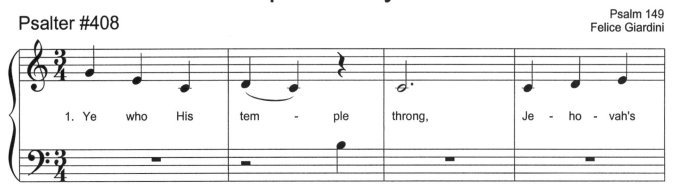

1. Ye who His tem - ple throng, Jehovah's

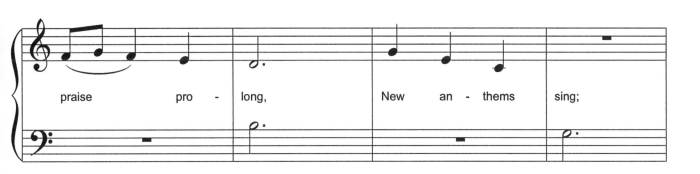

praise pro - long, New an - thems sing;

Ye saints, with joy de - clare Your Mak - er's lov - ing care,

And let the chil - dren there Joy in their King.

Our Lord Jesus

Psalter #302

Psalm 110
Charles H. Gabriel

1. The Lord un-to His Christ hath said, In glo-ry I en-throne Thee Till

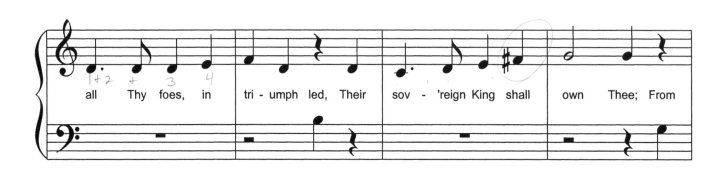

all Thy foes, in tri-umph led, Their sov-'reign King shall own Thee; From

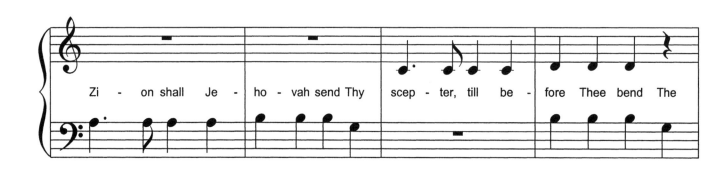

Zi-on shall Je-ho-vah send Thy scep-ter, till be-fore Thee bend The

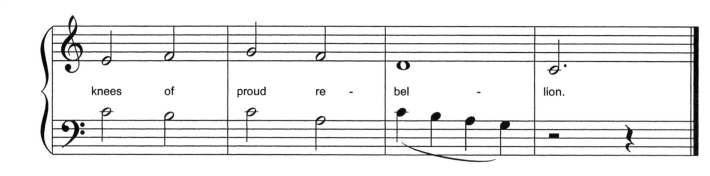

knees of proud re-bel - lion.

A Suppliant Church

Psalm 80
James Langran

Psalter #218

1. O Thou great Shep - herd of Thy cho - sen race, Who lead-est like a

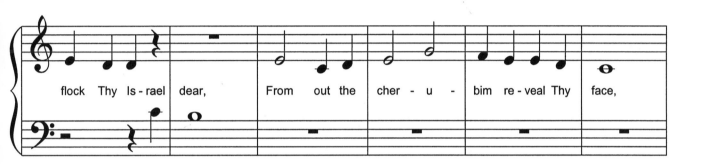

flock Thy Is - rael dear, From out the cher - u - bim re - veal Thy face,

Be - fore our host now let Thy might ap- pear. Come Thou, O God, to

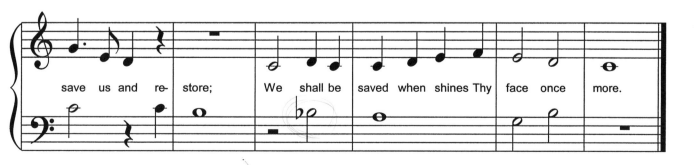

save us and re- store; We shall be saved when shines Thy face once more.

Acceptable Worship

Psalm 50
Arranged from Bortniansky

Psalter #137

1. The might - y God, Je - ho - vah, speaks And

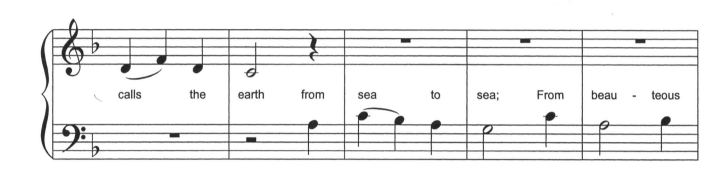

calls the earth from sea to sea; From beau - teous

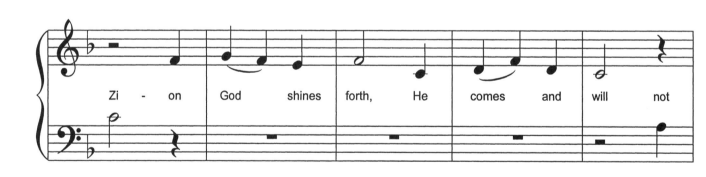

Zi - on God shines forth, He comes and will not

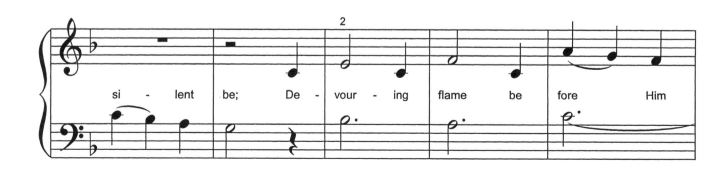

si - lent be; De - vour - ing flame be - fore Him

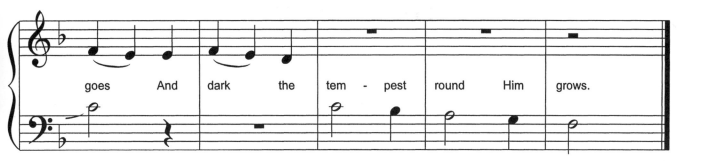

goes And dark the tem - pest round Him grows.

The Ascended King

Psalm 47
Isaac Smith

Psalter #130

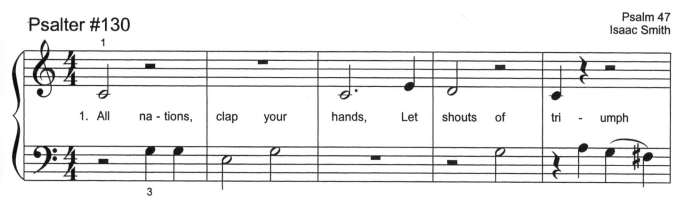

1. All na - tions, clap your hands, Let shouts of tri - umph

ring, For might - y o - ver all the

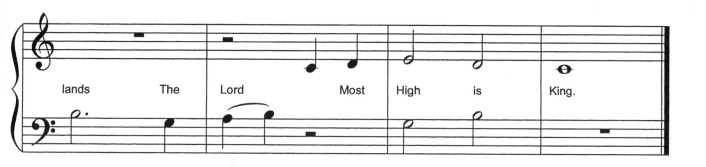

lands The Lord Most High is King.

The Righteous Judgment of God

Psalter #206

Psalm 75
Uzziah C. Burnap

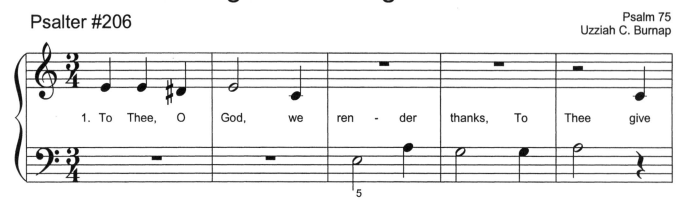

1. To Thee, O God, we ren - der thanks, To Thee give

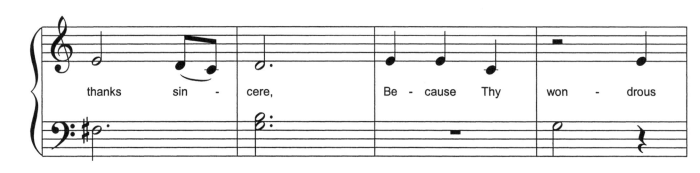

thanks sin - cere, Be - cause Thy won - drous

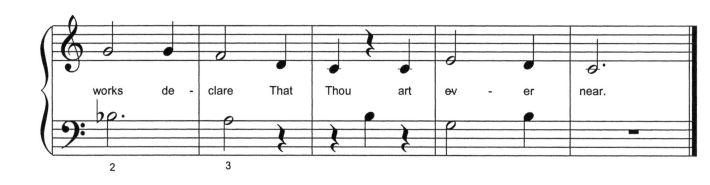

works de - clare That Thou art ev - er near.

The Protective Power of God

Psalter #127

Psalm 46
J. Baptiste Calkin

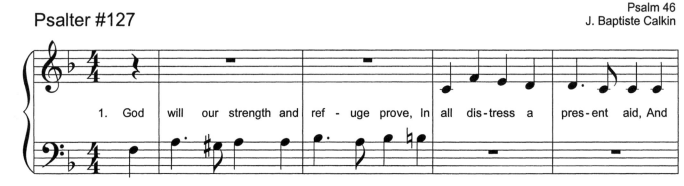

1. God will our strength and ref - uge prove, In all dis-tress a pres - ent aid, And

though the trem - bling earth re-move, We will not fear nor be dis-mayed.

5

Suffering and Prayer

Psalter #184

Psalm 69
Isaac B. Woodbury

1. Save me, O God, be - cause the floods Come in up -

on my soul; I sink in depths where none can

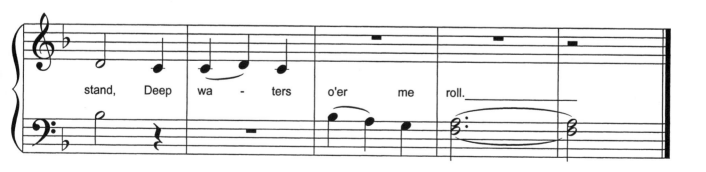

stand, Deep wa - ters o'er me roll.

Exultation in God

Psalm 138
William B. Bradbury

Psalter #381

1. With grate-ful heart my thanks I bring, Be - fore the great Thy praise I sing; I

wor-ship in Thy ho - ly place And praise Thee for Thy truth and grace; For truth and grace to -

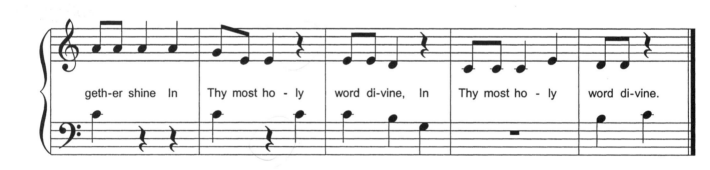

geth-er shine In Thy most ho - ly word di-vine, In Thy most ho - ly word di-vine.

An Ideal Worshiper

Psalm 15
The Parish Choir

Psalter #26

1. Who, O Lord, shall dwell with Thee In the tem-ple of Thy grace?

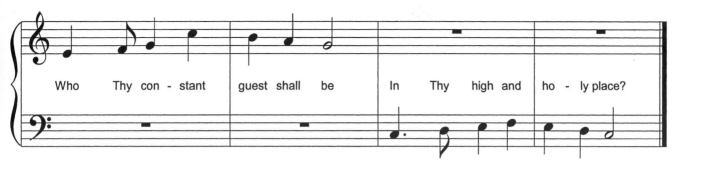

Who Thy con - stant guest shall be In Thy high and ho - ly place?

Confession of Trust

Psalm 55
Luther O. Emerson

Psalter #149

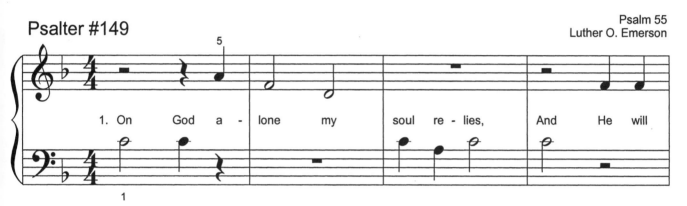

1. On God a - lone my soul re - lies, And He will

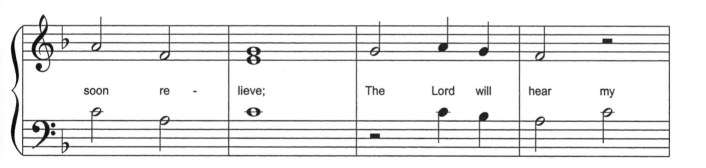

soon re - lieve; The Lord will hear my

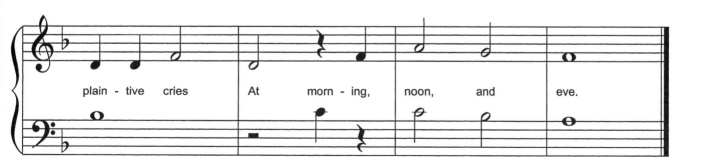

plain - tive cries At morn - ing, noon, and eve.

The Duty of Praise

Psalter #250

Psalm 92
Ernest R. Kroeger

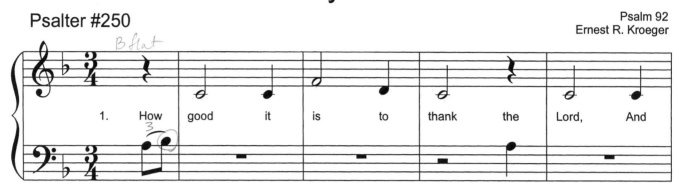

1. How good it is to thank the Lord, And

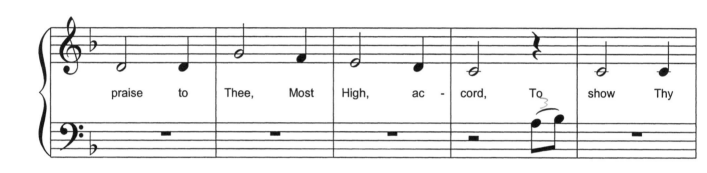

praise to Thee, Most High, ac - cord, To show Thy

love with morn - ing light, And tell Thy faith - ful -

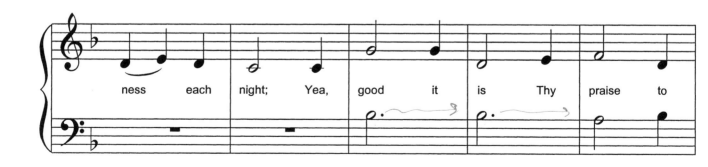

ness each night; Yea, good it is Thy praise to

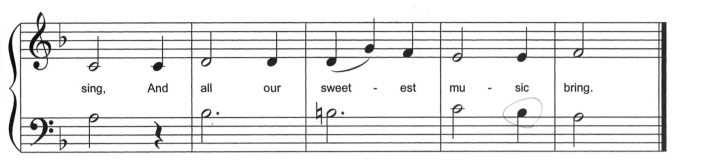

sing, And all our sweet - est mu - sic bring.

The Glory of the Church

Psalter #131

Psalm 48
Arranged from Haydn

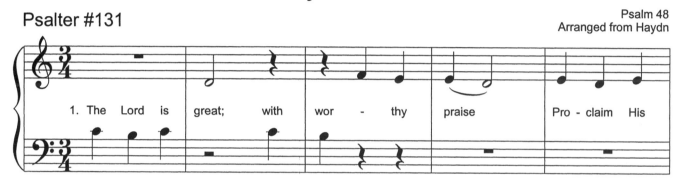

1. The Lord is great; with wor - thy praise Pro - claim His

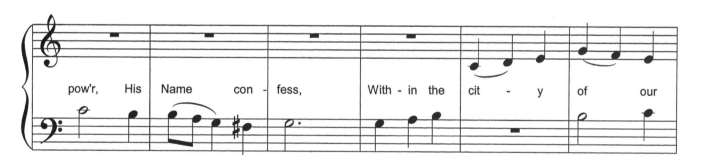

pow'r, His Name con - fess, With - in the cit - y of our

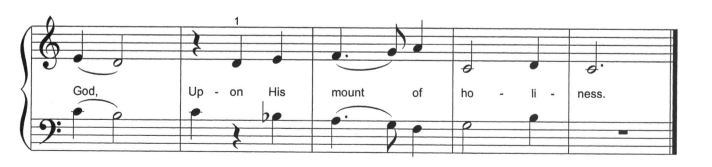

God, Up - on His mount of ho - li - ness.

A Mourner's Entreaties

Psalm 39
Joseph E. Sweetser

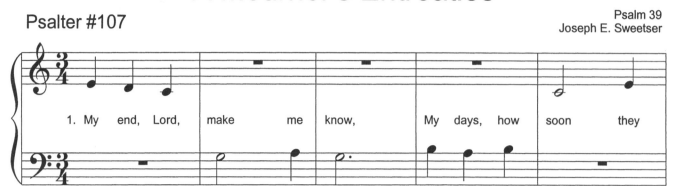

1. My end, Lord, make me know, My days, how soon they

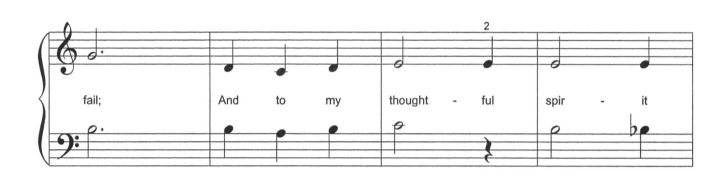

fail; And to my thought - ful spir - it

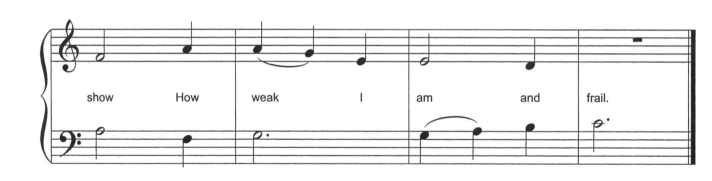

show How weak I am and frail.

The Prayer of the Righteous

Psalter #31

Psalm 17
Thomas Hastings

1. Lord, hear the right, re - gard my cry, My prayer from

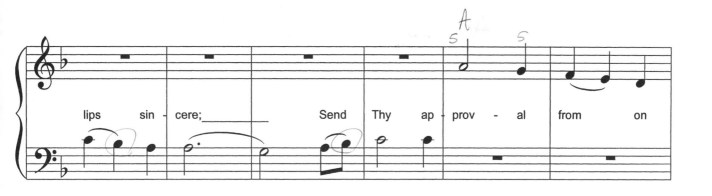

lips sin - cere;_____ Send Thy ap - prov - al from on

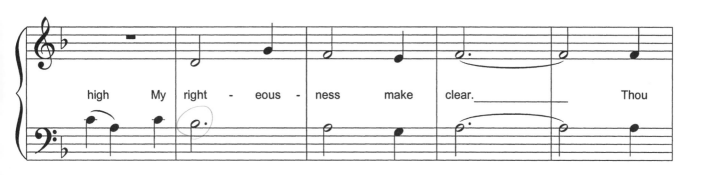

high My right - eous - ness make clear._____ Thou

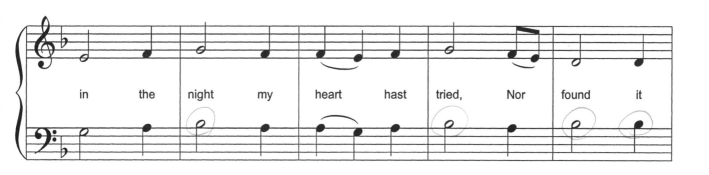

in the night my heart hast tried, Nor found it

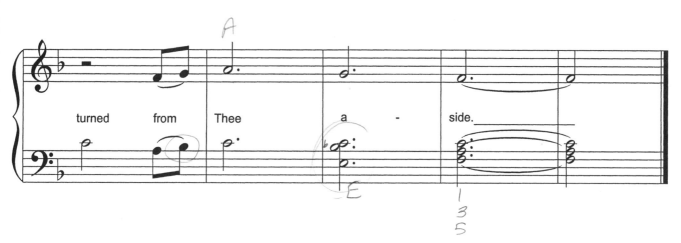

turned from Thee a - side._____

The Sovereign of the Sea

Psalm 107
H. A. Cesar Malan

Psalter #295

1. They that traf - fic on the sea, While un - ceas - ing

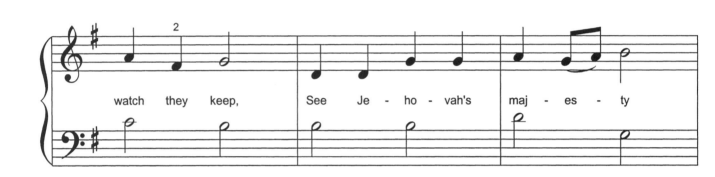

watch they keep, See Je - ho - vah's maj - es - ty

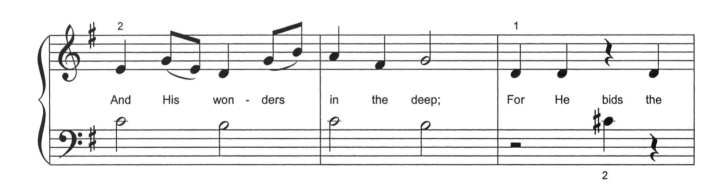

And His won - ders in the deep; For He bids the

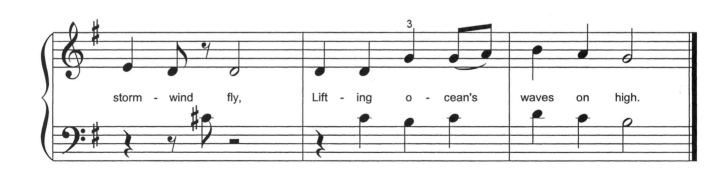

storm - wind fly, Lift - ing o - cean's waves on high.

Longing and Confession

Psalm 119
Lowell Mason

Psalter #342

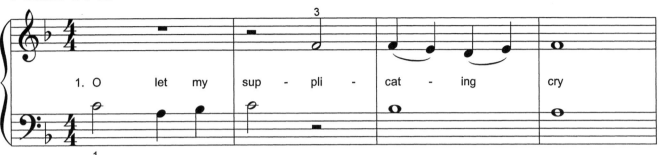

1. O let my sup - pli - cat - ing cry

By Thee, my gra - cious Lord, be heard;

Give wis - dom and de - liv - er me

Ac - cord - ing to Thy faith - ful word.

God's Strength Our Protection

Psalter #34

Psalm 18
German Melody

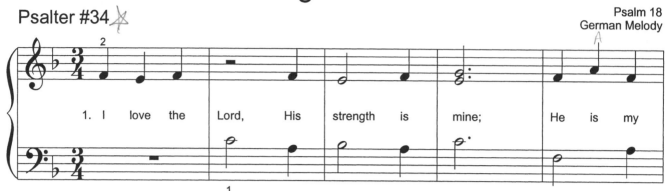

1. I love the Lord, His strength is mine; He is my

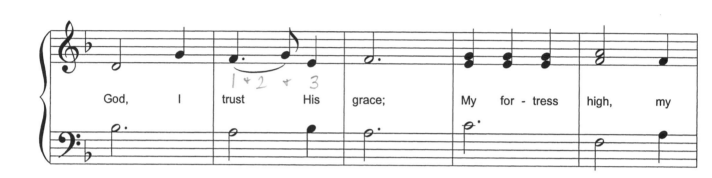

God, I trust His grace; My for - tress high, my

shield di - vine, My Sav - iour and my hid - ing - place.

Invocation and Confident Petition

Psalter #75

Psalm 28
Darius E. Jones

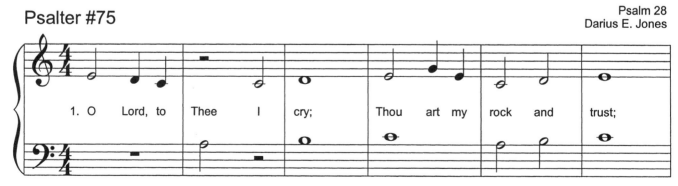

1. O Lord, to Thee I cry; Thou art my rock and trust;

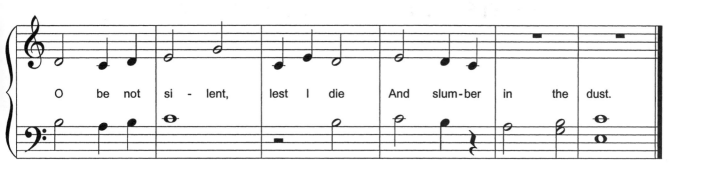

The Cross of Calvary

Psalm 22
Lowell Mason

Psalter #47

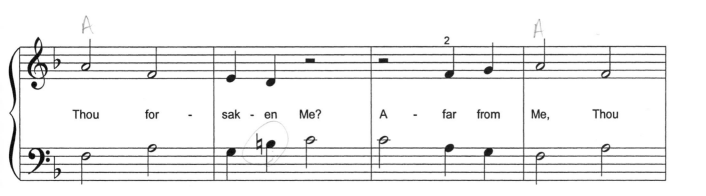

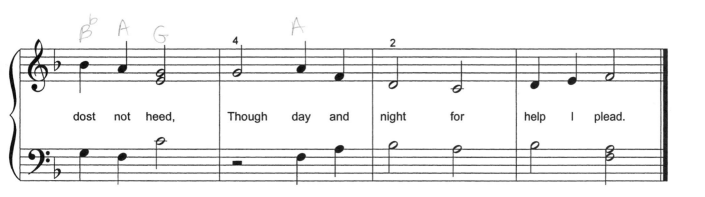

The House of God

Psalter #368

Psalm 132
Henry K. Oliver

1. A - rise, O Lord, our God, a - rise

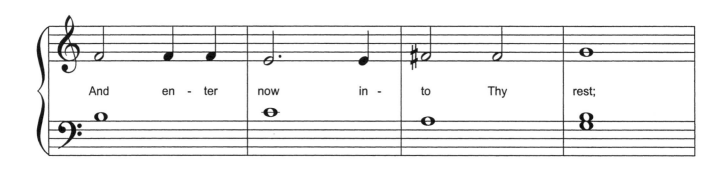

And en - ter now in - to Thy rest;

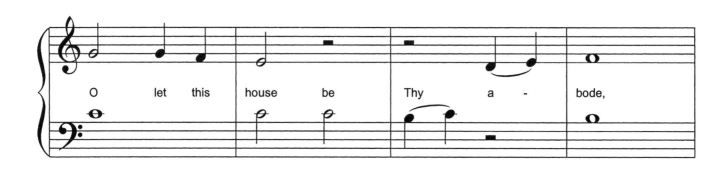

O let this house be Thy a - bode,

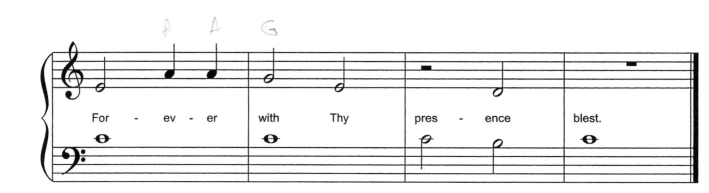

For - ev - er with Thy pres - ence blest.

Praise-Voices

Psalm 148
George C. Stebbins

Psalter #405

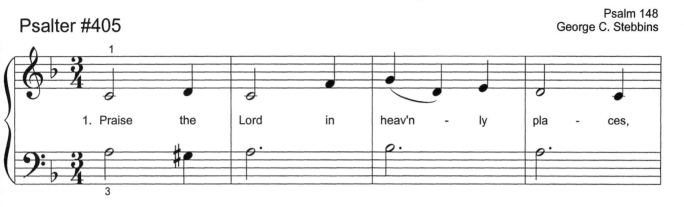

1. Praise the Lord in heav'n - ly pla - ces,

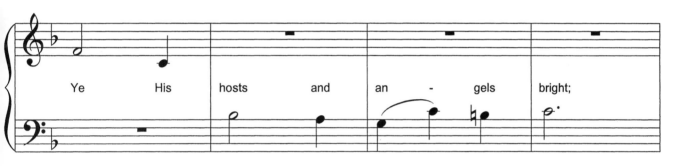

Ye His hosts and an - gels bright;

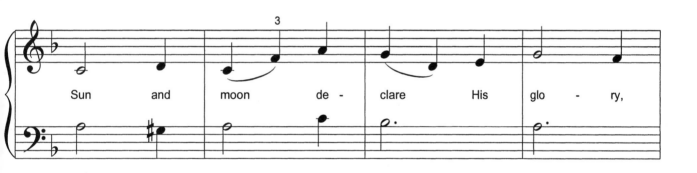

Sun and moon de - clare His glo - ry,

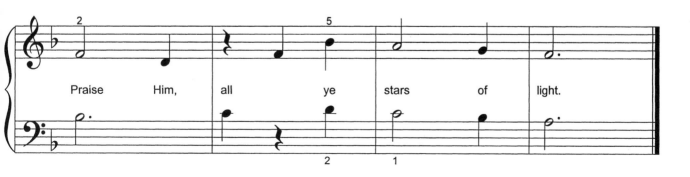

Praise Him, all ye stars of light.

Our Glorious King

Psalter #394

Psalm 145
Arranged by Arthur S. Sullivan

1. I will ex - tol Thee, O my God, And praise Thee, O my

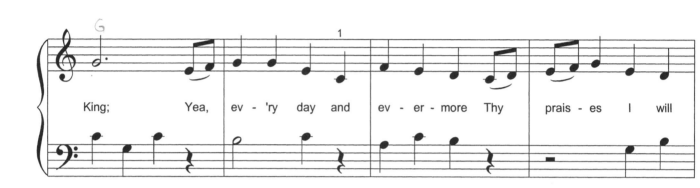

King; Yea, ev - 'ry day and ev - er - more Thy prais - es I will

sing. Great is the Lord, our might - y God, And great - ly to be praised; His

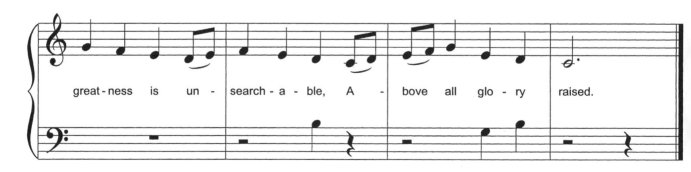

great - ness is un - search - a - ble, A - bove all glo - ry raised.

-100-

Trust in the Mercy of God

Psalm 13
Alexander B. Morton

Psalter #22

1. How long wilt Thou for - get me, O Lord, Thou God of grace? How

long shall fears be - set me While dark - ness hides Thy face? How

long shall griefs dis - tress me And turn my day to night? How

long shall foes op - press me And tri - umph in their might?

Forgiving Mercy Besought

Psalter #217

Psalm 79
Arranged from Beethoven

1. Re - mem - ber not, O God, The sins of long a - go; In

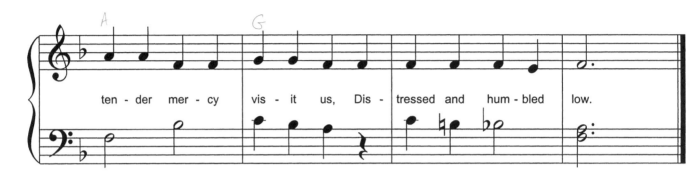

ten - der mer - cy vis - it us, Dis - tressed and hum - bled low.

Dependence on God

Psalter #161

Psalm 62
James Walch

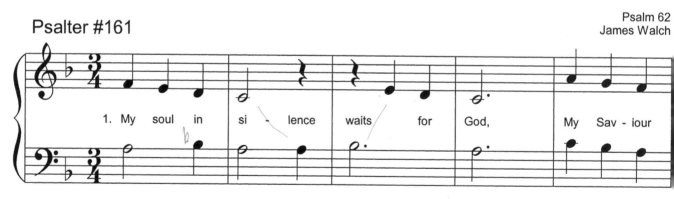

1. My soul in si - lence waits for God, My Sav - iour

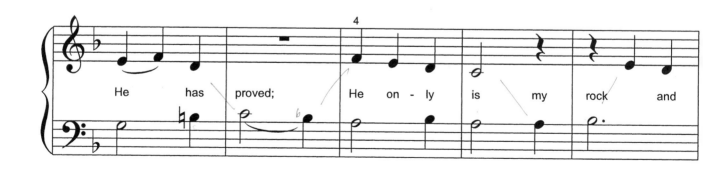

He has proved; He on - ly is my rock and

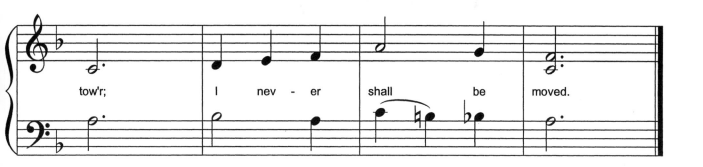

tow'r; I nev - er shall be moved.

Nature's Tribute to God

Psalter #37

Psalm 19
Arranged from John Goss

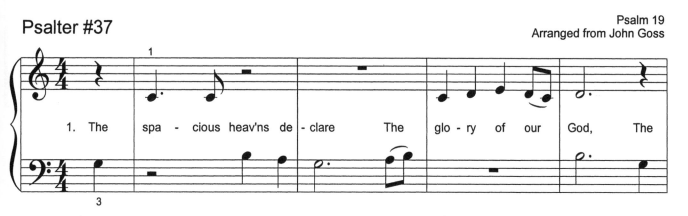

1. The spa - cious heav'ns de - clare The glo - ry of our God, The

fir - ma - ment dis - plays His hand - i - work a - broad; Day un - to day pro -

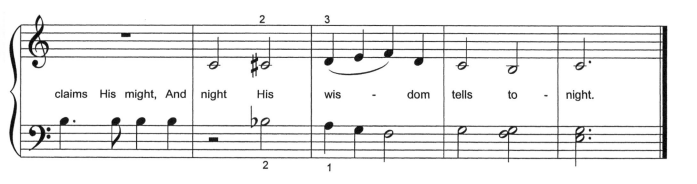

claims His might, And night His wis - dom tells to - night.

God the Giver of Victory

Psalter #121

Psalm 44
Anonymous

1. O God, we have heard and our fa - thers have told What

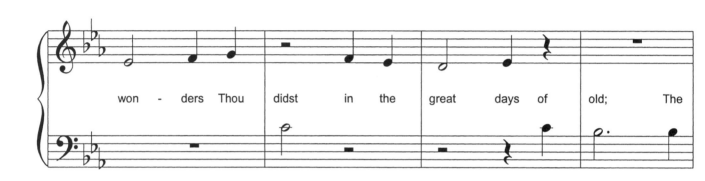

won - ders Thou didst in the great days of old; The

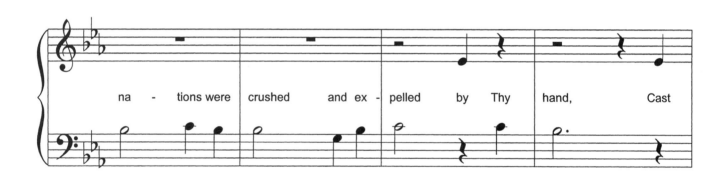

na - tions were crushed and ex - pelled by Thy hand, Cast

out that Thy peo - ple might dwell in their land.

Immortality and Resurrection

Psalter #29

Psalm 16
e William Martin

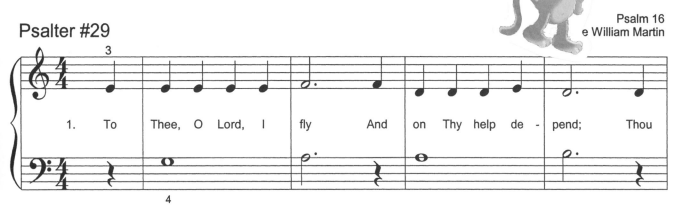

1. To Thee, O Lord, I fly And on Thy help de - pend; Thou

art my Lord and King Most High; Do Thou my soul de - fend. I

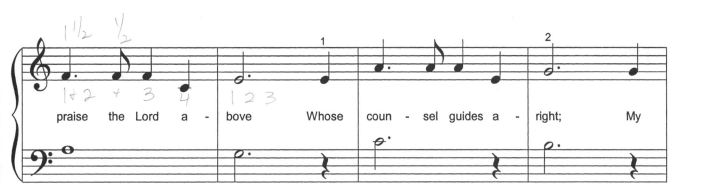

praise the Lord a - bove Whose coun - sel guides a - right; My

heart in - structs me in His love In sea - sons of the night.

Prayer for the Oppressed

Psalm 10
C. Warwick Jordan

Psalter #19

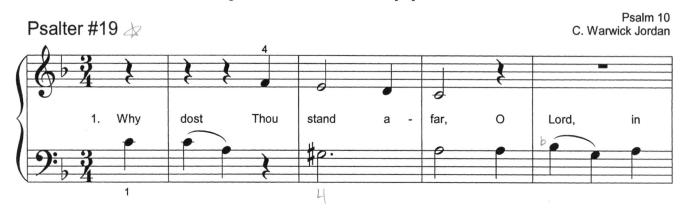

1. Why dost Thou stand a - far, O Lord, in

our dis - tress?_____ And why dost Thou con -

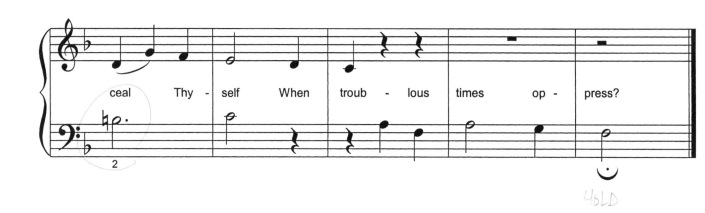

ceal Thy - self When troub - lous times op - press?

God Our Guardian

Psalm 3
Arthur Cottman

Psalter #5

1. O Lord, how are my foes in - creased! A - gainst me man - y rise; How

man - y say, In vain for help He on his God re - lies!

Importunate Prayer

Psalm 119
Anton Gersbach

Psalter #339

1. O Lord, my ear - nest cry Thy lis - t'ning ear has

heard; With Thy sal - va - tion an - swer me, And

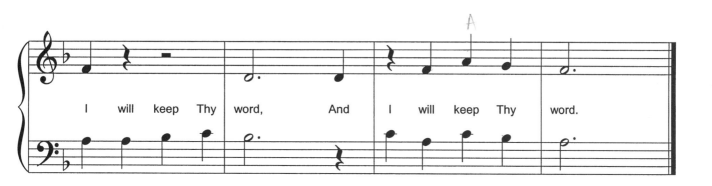

I will keep Thy word, And I will keep Thy word.

The Mercy of God Besought

Psalter #110

Psalm 40
W. Irving Hartshorn

1. Thy ten - der mer - cies, O my Lord, With - hold not, I im - plore; But

1/8 note = 1 beat   1/4 note = 2 beats

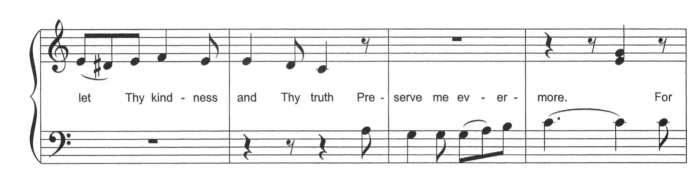

let Thy kind - ness and Thy truth Pre - serve me ev - er - more. For

count - less ills have com - passed me, My sin - ful deeds a - rise; Yea,

they have o - ver - tak - en me; I dare not raise my eyes.

Confidence in Divine Justice

Psalm 7
Arranged from Donizetti

Psalter #13

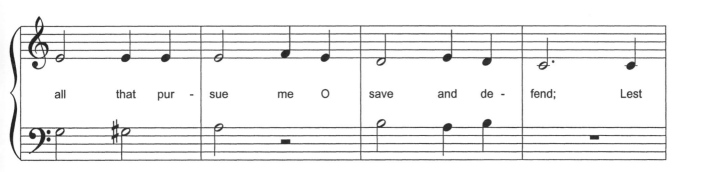

1. Je - ho - vah, my God, on Thy help I de - pend; From

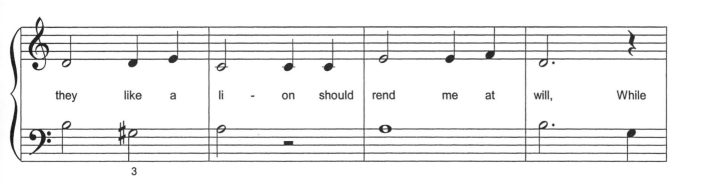

all that pur - sue me O save and de - fend; Lest

they like a li - on should rend me at will, While

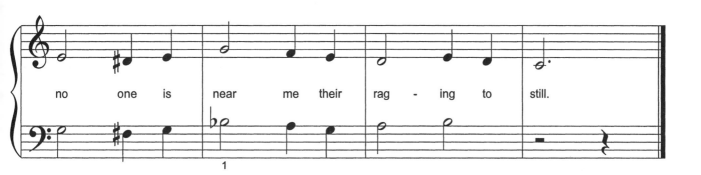

no one is near me their rag - ing to still.

Jesus Crowned and Triumphant

Psalm 21
E. G. Taylor

Psalter #45

1. Now the King in Thy strength shall be joy - ful, O Lord, Thy sal - va - tion shall

make Him re - joice;_____ For the wish of His heart Thou didst

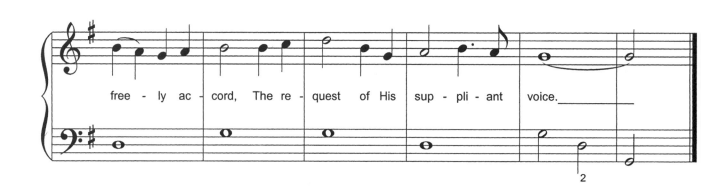

free - ly ac - cord, The re - quest of His sup - pli - ant voice._____

Granted Prayers

Psalm 116
Arranged from Carl G. Glaser

Psalter #312

1. I love the Lord Who heard my cry And grant - ed my re - quest; In

Him Who hears and an - swers prayer My trust thro' life shall rest.

Quieting Thoughts

Psalm 4
Spencer Lane

Psalter #7

1. On the good and faith - ful God has set His love; When they call He sends them

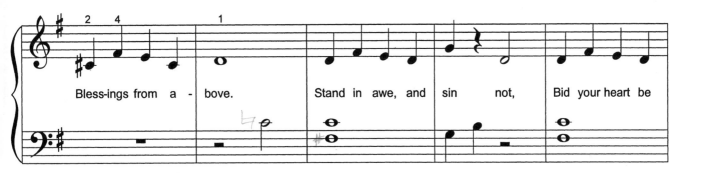

Bless-ings from a - bove. Stand in awe, and sin not, Bid your heart be

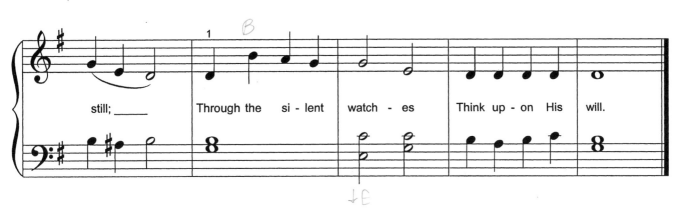

still; _____ Through the si - lent watch - es Think up - on His will.

Contrasted Characters

Psalm 37
William Hayes

Psalter #96

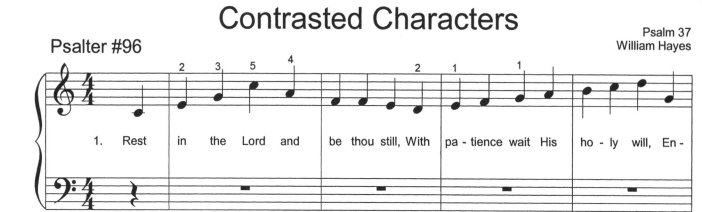

1. Rest in the Lord and be thou still, With pa - tience wait His ho - ly will, En -

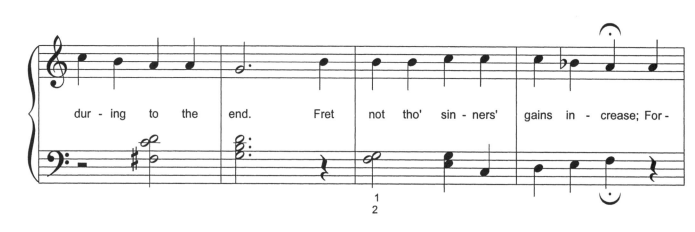

dur - ing to the end. Fret not tho' sin - ners' gains in - crease; For -

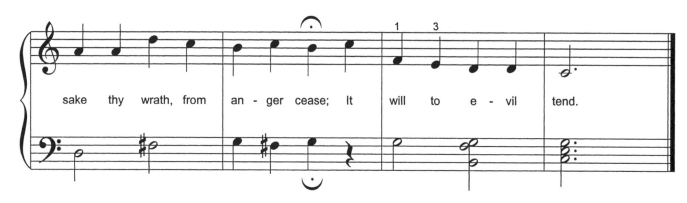

sake thy wrath, from an - ger cease; It will to e - vil tend.

The Blessings of the God-Fearing

Psalm 25
Alberto Randegger

Psalter #65

1. Grace and truth shall mark the way Where the Lord His own will lead,

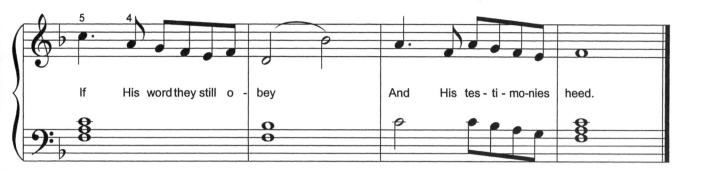

If His word they still o - bey   And His tes - ti - mo - nies heed.

Gracious Guidance

Psalter #84

Psalm 32
Isaac B. Woodbury

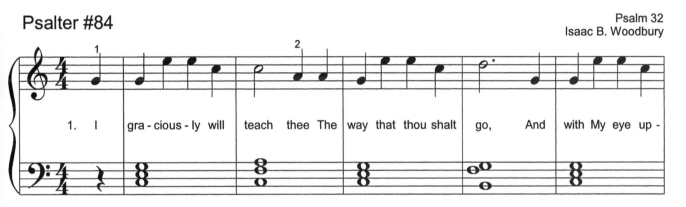

1. I gra - cious - ly will teach thee The way that thou shalt go,   And with My eye up -

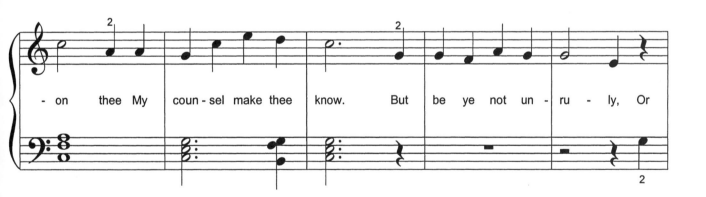

- on thee My coun - sel make thee know.   But be ye not un - ru - ly, Or

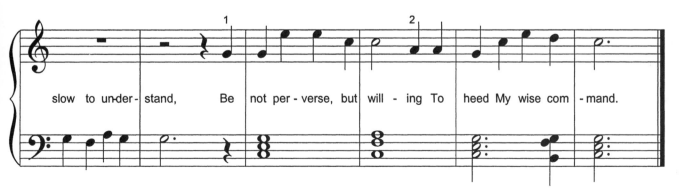

slow to un - der - stand,   Be not per - verse, but will - ing To heed My wise com - mand.

Assurances for Evil Days

Psalm 12
Thomas Hastings

Psalter #21

1. O Lord, be Thou my help - er true, For

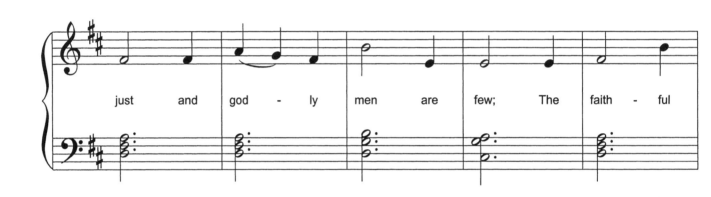

just and god - ly men are few; The faith - ful

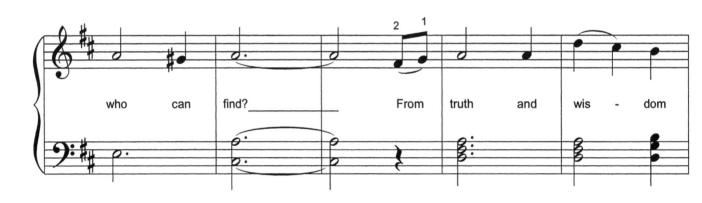

who can find?_____ From truth and wis - dom

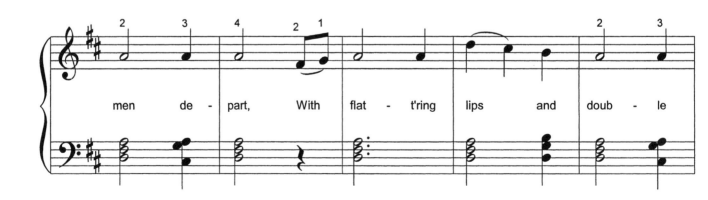

men de - part, With flat - t'ring lips and doub - le

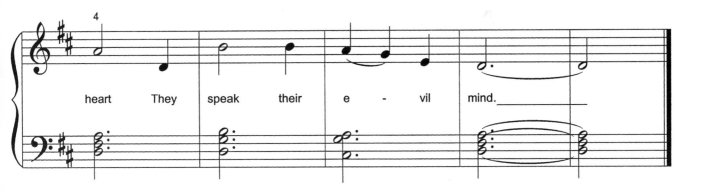

heart They speak their e - vil mind.

Mutual Intercession

Psalter #43

Psalm 20
Arranged by Lowell Mason

1. Je - ho - vah hear thee in thy grief, Our fa - thers'

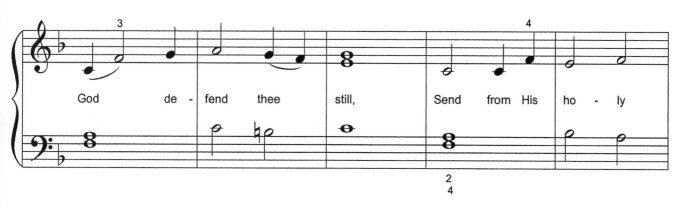

God de - fend thee still, Send from His ho - ly

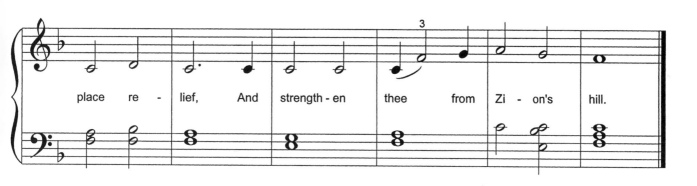

place re - lief, And strength - en thee from Zi - on's hill.

Holiness and Divine Favor

Psalter #35

Psalm 18
W. St. Clair Palmer

1. Since with my God with per-fect heart I walk and make His word my guide, And from in-iq - ui - ty de - part, The Lord His bless - ing will pro - vide.

The Name of the Lord

Psalter #14

Psalm 8
Joseph P. Holbrook

1. O Lord, our Lord, in all the earth How ex-cel - lent Thy Name!

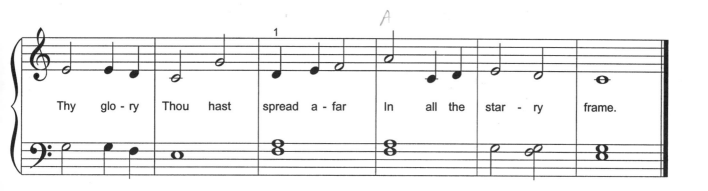

Thy glo - ry Thou hast spread a - far In all the star - ry frame.

Prayer for Defense and Guidance

Psalm 25
Arranged from Hans G. Nageli

Psalter #60

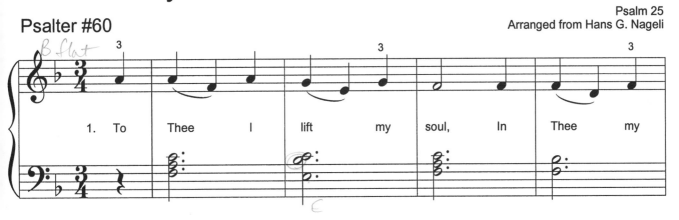

1. To Thee I lift my soul, In Thee my

trust re - pose; My God, O put me

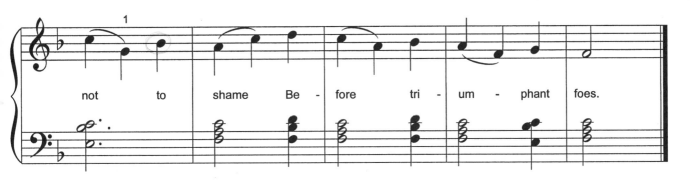

not to shame Be - fore tri - um - phant foes.

Pardoning Mercy

Psalter #365

Psalm 130
Ethelbert W. Bullinger

1. From the depths my prayer as - cend - eth Un - to

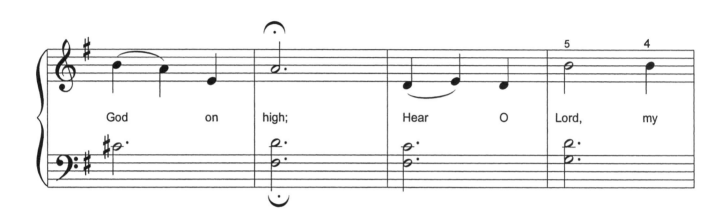

God on high; Hear O Lord, my

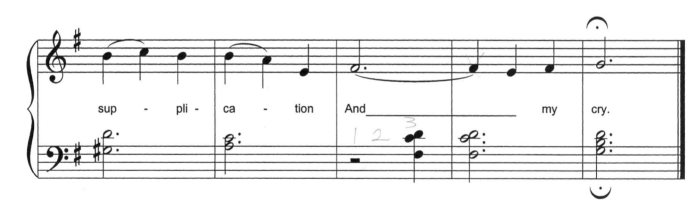

sup - pli - ca - tion And_____ my cry.

The Searcher of Hearts

Psalm 139
Anonymous

Psalter #384

1. O Lord, my in - most heart and thought Thy

search - ing eye doth see; Wher - e'er I rest, wher -

e'er I go, My ways are known to Thee.

The Searcher of Hearts

Psalm 139
William Horsley

Psalter #384 - second tune

1. O Lord, my in - most heart and thought Thy search-ing eye doth see; Wher -

e'er I rest, wher - e'er I go, My ways are known to Thee.

Divine Power in Manifestation

Psalm 29
Charles H. Gabriel

Psalter #76

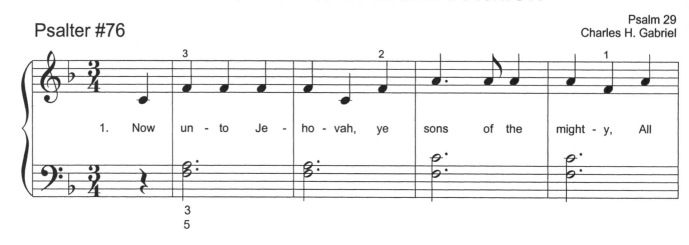

1. Now un - to Je - ho - vah, ye sons of the might - y, All

glo - ry and strength and do - min - ion ac - cord; As -

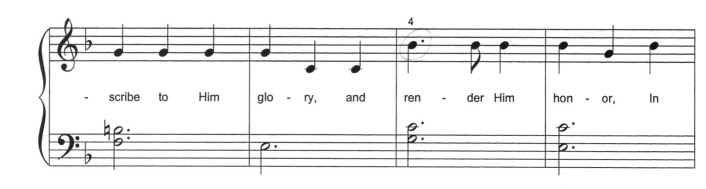

- scribe to Him glo - ry, and ren - der Him hon - or, In

beau - ty of ho - li - ness wor - ship the Lord.

The Praise of the Redeemed

Psalter #297

Psalm 107
Lowell Mason

1. O praise the Lord, for He is good, His mer - cies still en - dure; Thus

let His ran - somed tes - ti - fy, From all their foes se - cure. He

has re - deemed His cap - tive saints From ad - ver - sa - ries' hands, Has

gath - ered them and brought them back In peace from hos - tile lands.

The Profit of Bible Study

Psalter #333

Psalm 119
William B. Bradbury

1. How I love Thy law, O Lord! Dai - ly

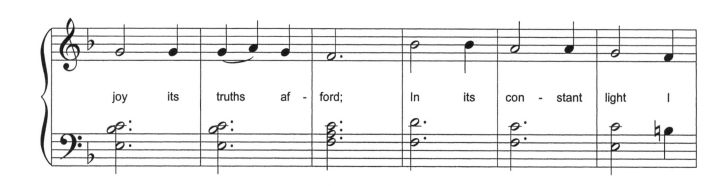

joy its truths af - ford; In its con - stant light I

go, Wise to con - quer ev - 'ry foe.

A Mindful God

Psalter #281

Psalm 103
Isaac B. Woodbury

1. Mind - ful of our hu - man frail - ty Is the God in Whom we trust; He Whose

years are ev-er- last - ing, He re- mem- bers we are dust.

God Our Only Good

Psalter #204

Psalm 73
Lowell Mason

1. O God, how good Thou art To all the pure of heart,

Tho' life seems vain; Bur - dened with anx - ious care, I groped in

dark des - pair, Till in Thy house of prayer All was made plain.

God in Nature

Psalter #171

Psalm 65
George J. Webb

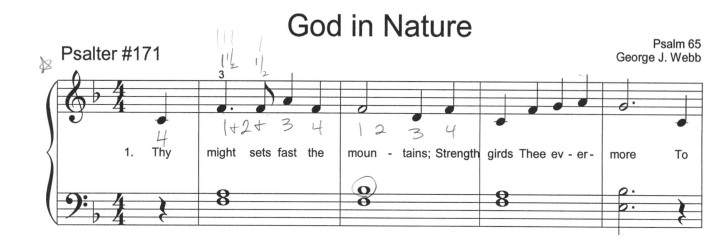

1. Thy might sets fast the moun - tains; Strength girds Thee ev - er- more To

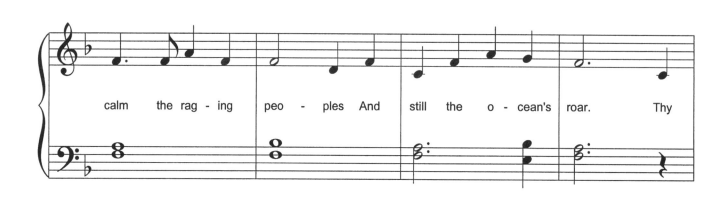

calm the rag - ing peo - ples And still the o - cean's roar. Thy

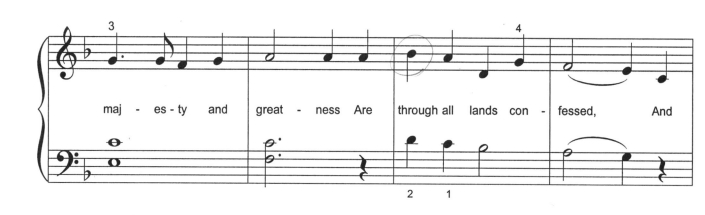

maj - es - ty and great - ness Are through all lands con - fessed, And

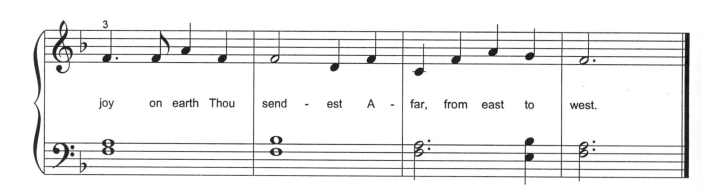

joy on earth Thou send - est A - far, from east to west.

The Majesty and Holiness of God

Psalm 99
German Melody

Psalter #265

1. Je - ho - vah reigns in maj - es - ty; Let all the na - tions quake. He

dwells be - tween the cher - u - bim; Let earth's foun - da - tions shake. Su -

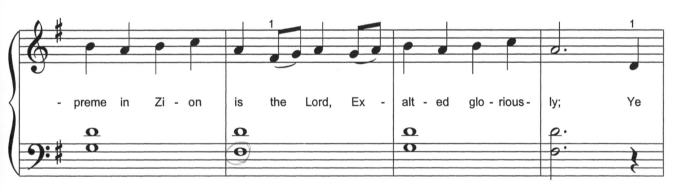

- preme in Zi - on is the Lord, Ex - alt - ed glo - rious - ly; Ye

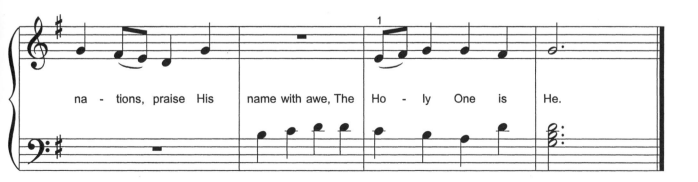

na - tions, praise His name with awe, The Ho - ly One is He.

Life with God

Psalm 73
William U. Butcher

Psalter #203

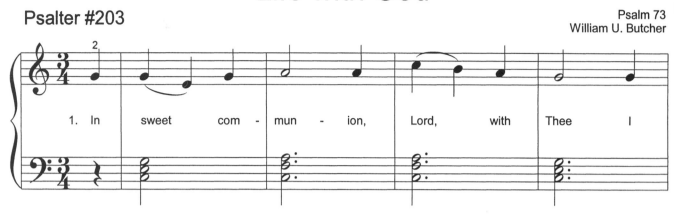

1. In sweet com - mun - ion, Lord, with Thee I

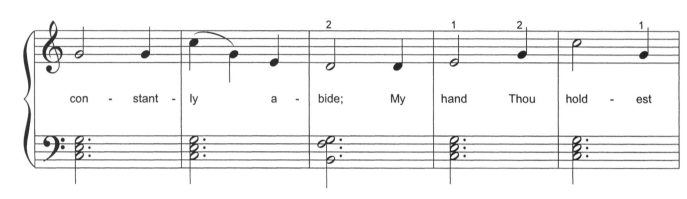

con - stant - ly a - bide; My hand Thou hold - est

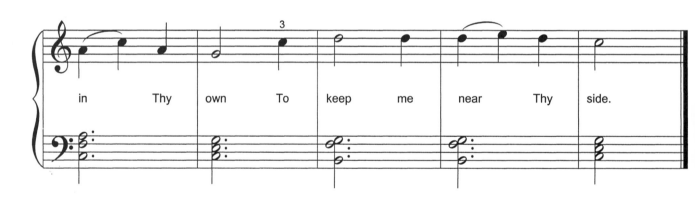

in Thy own To keep me near Thy side.

Prayerful Desire

Psalm 141
Henry Baker

Psalter #386

1. O Lord, make haste to hear my cry, To Thee I

call, on Thee re - ly; In - cline to me a

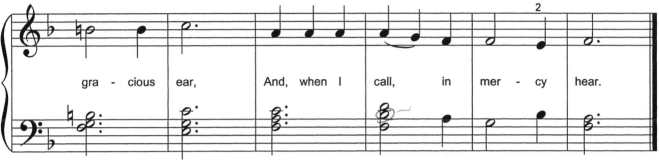

gra - cious ear, And, when I call, in mer - cy hear.

God the Righteous King

Psalm 99
Aaron Williams

Psalter #267

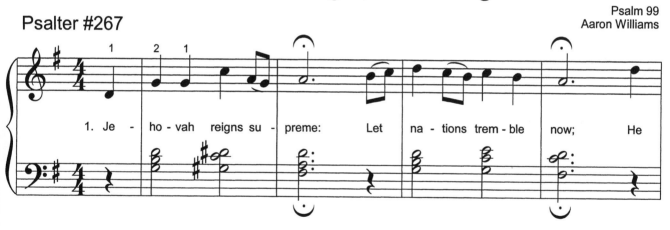

1. Je - ho - vah reigns su - preme: Let na - tions trem - ble now; He

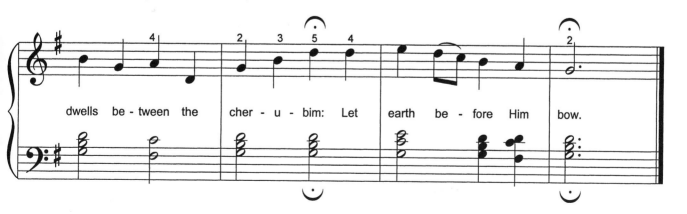

dwells be - tween the cher - u - bim: Let earth be - fore Him bow.

The Universal Debt of Praise

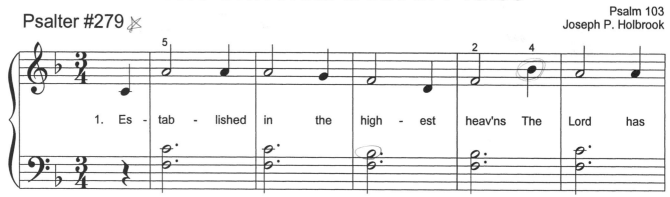

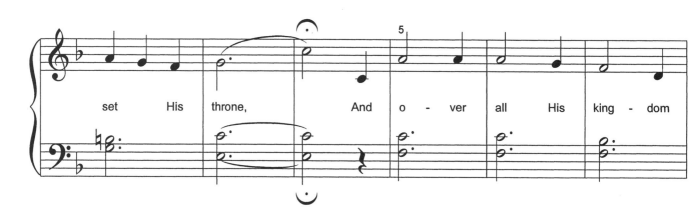

The Offering of Praise

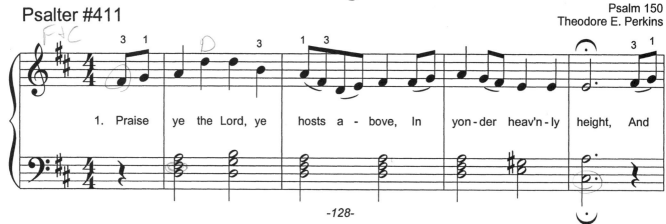

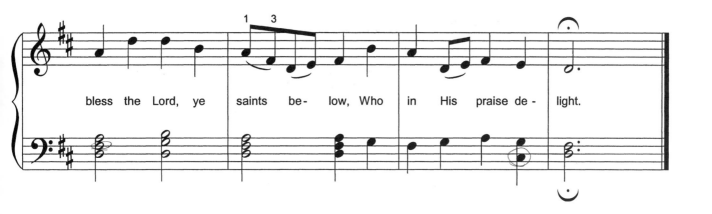

bless the Lord, ye saints be - low, Who in His praise de - light.

The Blessings of Immanuel's Reign

Psalter #198

Psalm 72
German Melody

1. O God, be Thy A - noint - ed Son With truth and

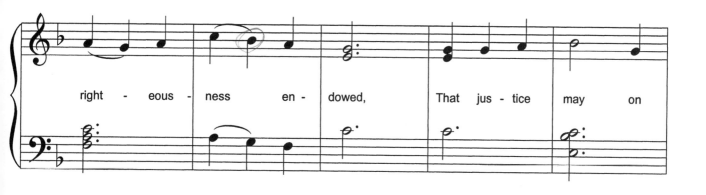

right - eous - ness en - dowed, That jus - tice may on

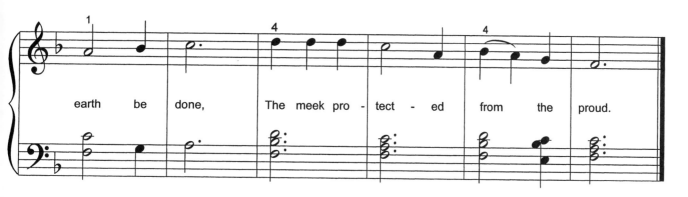

earth be done, The meek pro - tect - ed from the proud.

God Our Only Good

Psalm 73
Joseph P. Holbrook

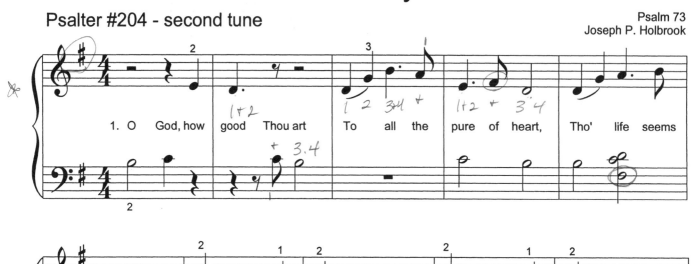

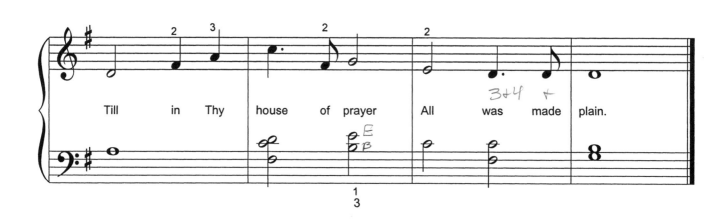

Family Happiness

Psalm 128
William H. Jude

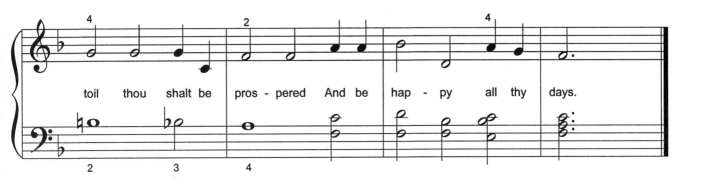

toil thou shalt be pros - pered And be hap - py all thy days.

The Promise of Victory

Psalm 149
Henry J. Gauntlett

Psalter #407

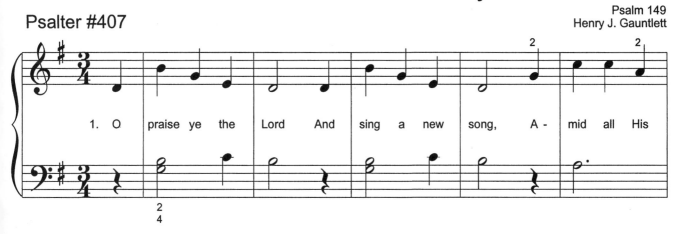

1. O praise ye the Lord And sing a new song, A - mid all His

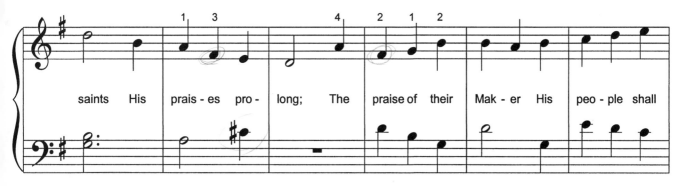

saints His prais - es pro - long; The praise of their Mak - er His peo - ple shall

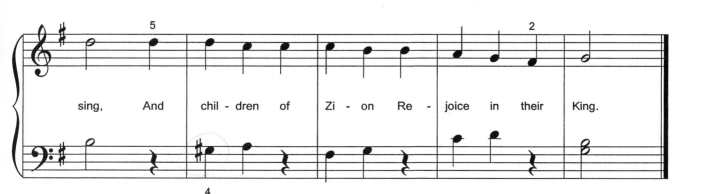

sing, And chil - dren of Zi - on Re - joice in their King.

Our Unsleeping Guardian

Psalter #345

Psalm 121
Marcus M. Wells

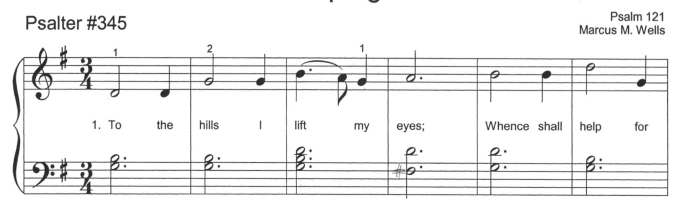

1. To the hills I lift my eyes; Whence shall help for

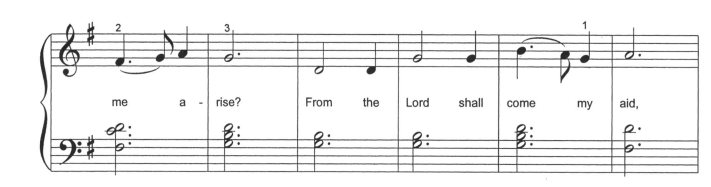

me a - rise? From the Lord shall come my aid,

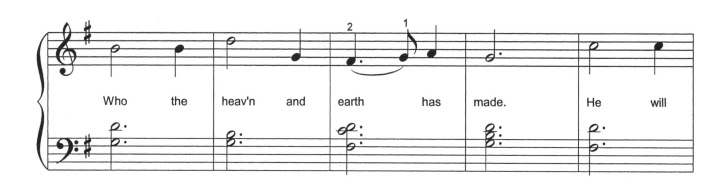

Who the heav'n and earth has made. He will

guide through dan - gers all, Will not suf - fer

thee to fall; He Who safe His peo - ple

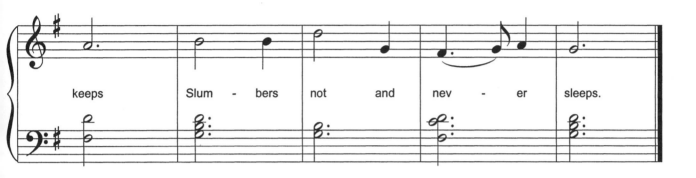

keeps Slum - bers not and nev - er sleeps.

Rescue from Spiritual Bondage

Psalter #357

Psalm 126
W. Martin

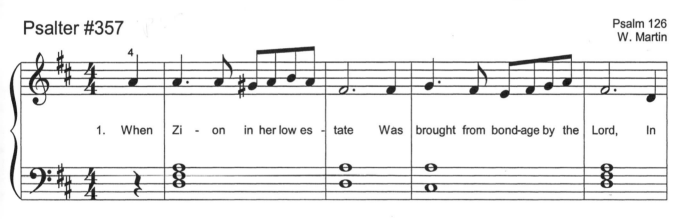

1. When Zi - on in her low es - tate Was brought from bond-age by the Lord, In

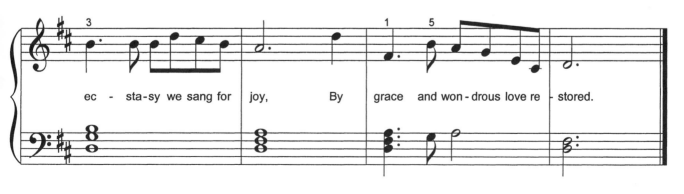

ec - sta-sy we sang for joy, By grace and won - drous love re - stored.

Quiet Trust

Psalter #344

Psalm 121
John B. Dykes

1. I to the hills will lift my eyes; O whence shall

come my aid? My help is from the Lord a -

lone. Who heav'n and earth has made.

A Summons to Praise

Psalter #409

Psalm 150
Lizzie S. Tourjee

1. Hal - le - lu - jah! Hal - le - lu - jah! In His tem - ple God be praised;

In the high and heav'n-ly pla - ces Be the sound - ing an - them raised.

The Greatness and Grace of God

Psalter #397

Psalm 145
John Hatton

1. O Lord, Thou art my God and King, And I will ev - er bless Thy Name; I will ex - tol Thee ev - 'ry day, And ev - er - more Thy praise pro - claim.

Remembrance of Church Privileges

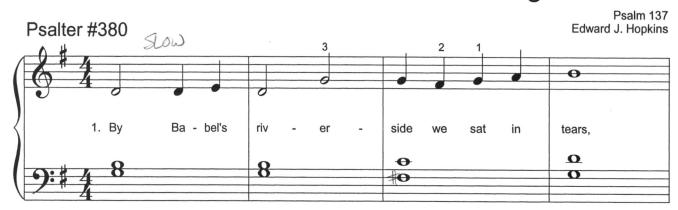

Psalter #380

slow

Psalm 137
Edward J. Hopkins

1. By Ba - bel's riv - er - side we sat in tears,

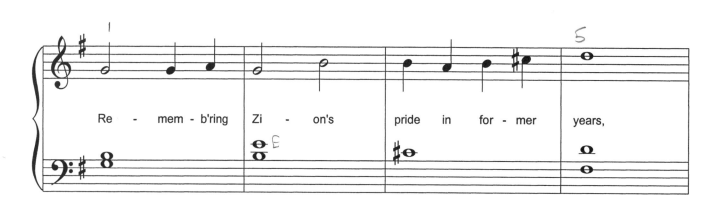

Re - mem - b'ring Zi - on's pride in for - mer years,

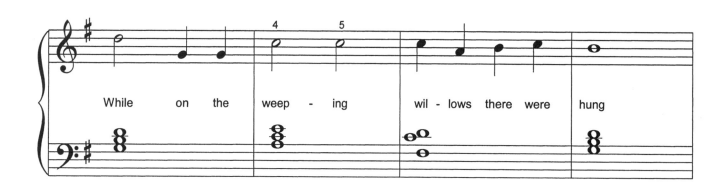

While on the weep - ing wil - lows there were hung

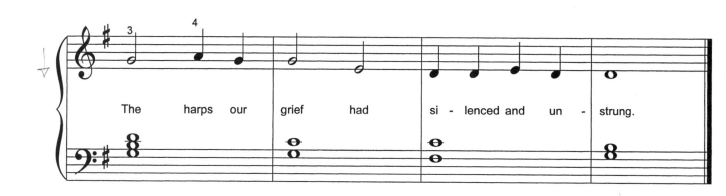

The harps our grief had si - lenced and un - strung.

Lessons from the Past

Psalm 78
Charles H. Gabriel

Psalter #213

1. My peo - ple, give ear, at - tend to my word, In

par - a - bles new deep truths shall be heard; The

won - der - ful sto - ry our fa - thers made known To

chil - dren suc - ceed - ing by us must be shown.

Grateful Adoration

Psalm 72
E. H. Frost

Psalter #196

1. Blest be the Lord, our fa - thers' God, E - ter - nal

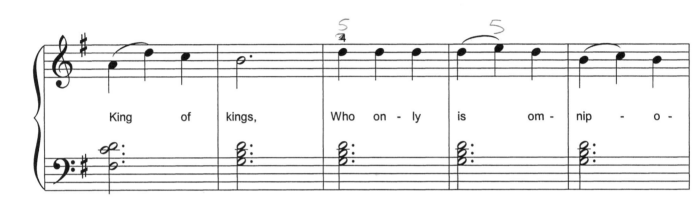

King of kings, Who on - ly is om - nip - o -

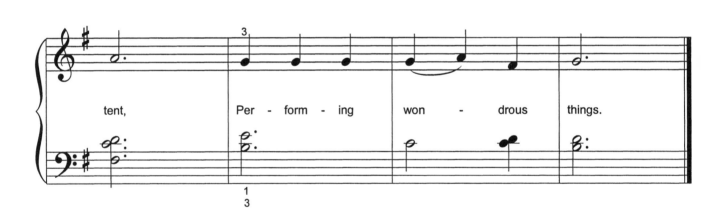

tent, Per - form - ing won - drous things.

God Our Help and Hope

Psalm 90
John B. Herbert

Psalter #247

1. O God, our help in a - ges past, Our hope for years to come, Our

shel - ter from the storm - y blast, And our e - ter - nal home.

Overshadowing Protection

Psalter #248

Psalm 91
William B. Bradbury

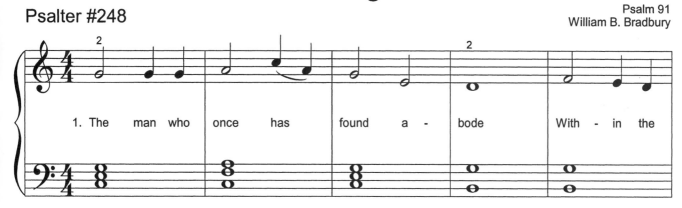

1. The man who once has found a - bode With - in the

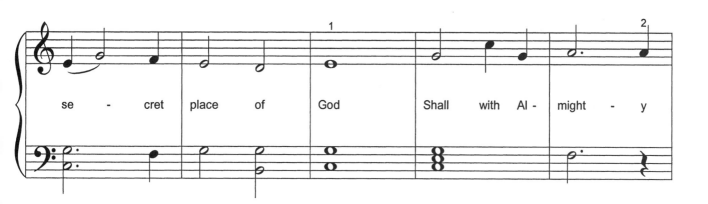

se - cret place of God Shall with Al - might - y

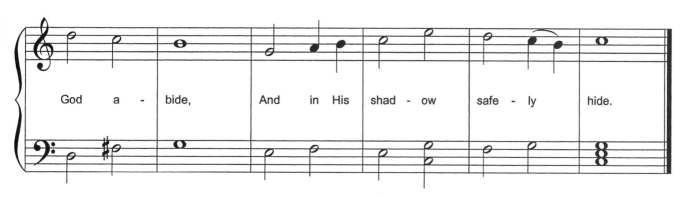

God a - bide, And in His shad - ow safe - ly hide.

God Our Advocate and Judge

Psalter #92

Psalm 35
E. M. Clark

1. Be Thou my help - er in the strife, O Lord, my strong de - fend - er be; Thy might - y shield pro - tect my life, Thy spear con - front the en - e - my. A - mid the con - flict, O my Lord, Thy pre - cious prom - ise let me hear. The faith - ful

re - as-sur-ing word: I am thy Sav-iour, do not fear.

The Kingdom of Our Lord

Psalm 72
Arranged by James C. Wade

Psalter #194

1. His wide do - min - ion shall ex - tend From

sea to ut - most sea, And un - to earth's re -

- mot - est bounds His peace - ful rule shall be.

The Universal Sovereignty of Christ

Psalm 47
Charles Burney

Psalter #129

1. Re - joice, ye peo - ple, hom - age give, To

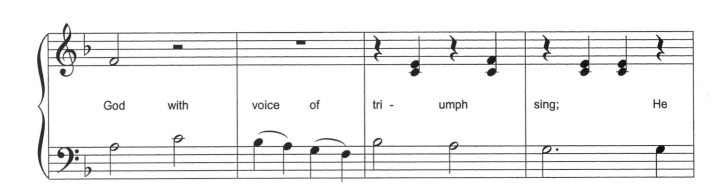

God with voice of tri - umph sing; He

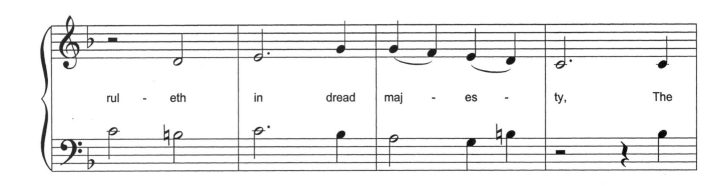

rul - eth in dread maj - es - ty, The

great, the u - ni - ver - sal King.

Longing for Revival

Psalm 80
Adoniram J. Gordon

Psalter #221

1. Great Shep - herd Who lead - est Thy peo - ple in love, 'Mid

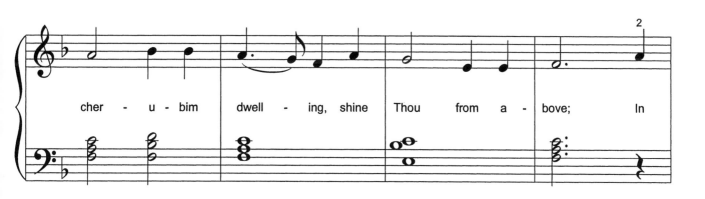

cher - u - bim dwell - ing, shine Thou from a - bove; In

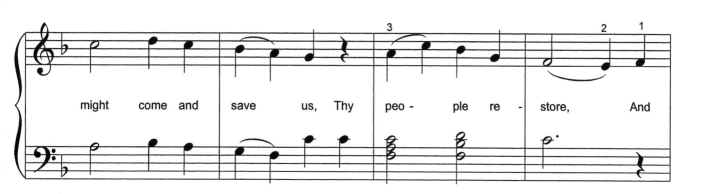

might come and save us, Thy peo - ple re - store, And

we shall be saved when Thy face shines once more.

The Love and Justice of God

Psalm 36
William B. Bradbury

Psalter #94

1. Thy mer - cy and Thy truth, O Lord, Tran - scend the

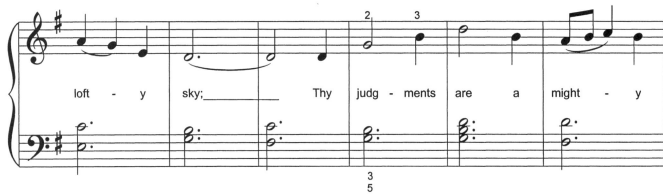

loft - y sky;_____ Thy judg - ments are a might - y

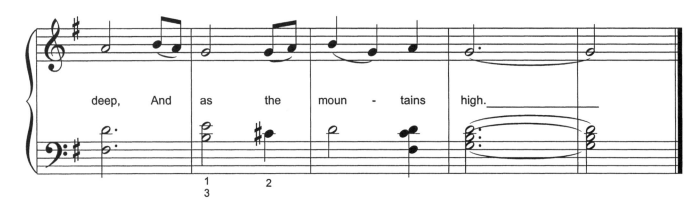

deep, And as the moun - tains high._____

God Our Resort in Trouble

Psalm 31
Nicholas Heins

Psalter #80

1. In Thee, O Lord, I put my trust, I call up - on Thy Name; O

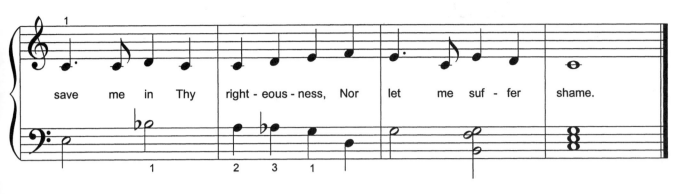

save me in Thy right-eous-ness, Nor let me suf-fer shame.

The Vanity of Trust in Riches

Psalm 49
Calvin S. Harrington

Psalter #135

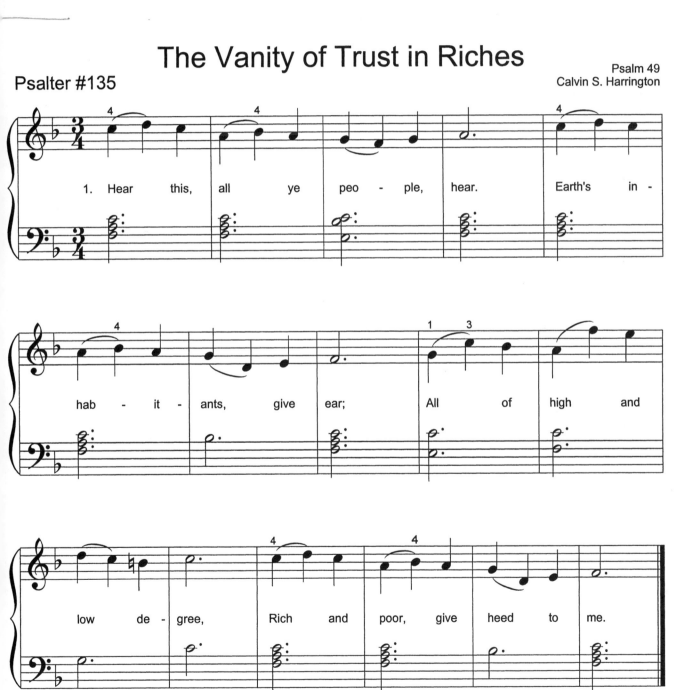

1. Hear this, all ye peo - ple, hear. Earth's in-

hab - it - ants, give ear; All of high and

low de - gree, Rich and poor, give heed to me.

Universal Adoration

Psalter #404

Psalm 148
William B. Bradbury

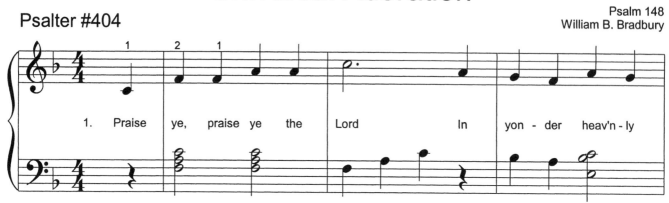

1. Praise ye, praise ye the Lord In yon - der heav'n - ly

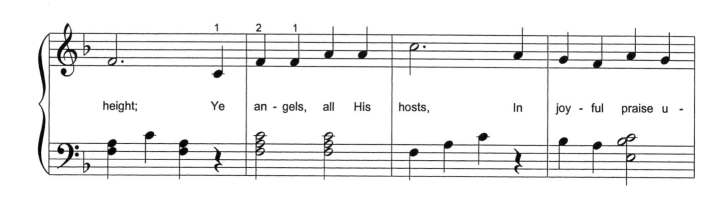

height; Ye an - gels, all His hosts, In joy - ful praise u -

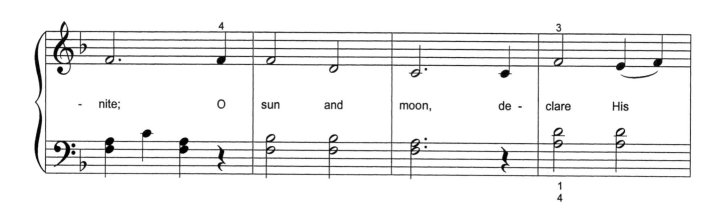

- nite; O sun and moon, de - clare His

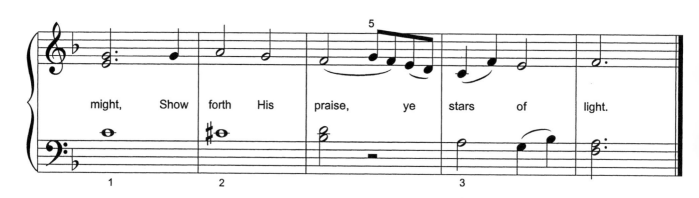

might, Show forth His praise, ye stars of light.

The Triumphs of the Gospel

Psalm 22
William H. Doane

Psalter #49

1. The ends of all the earth shall hear And turn un - to the

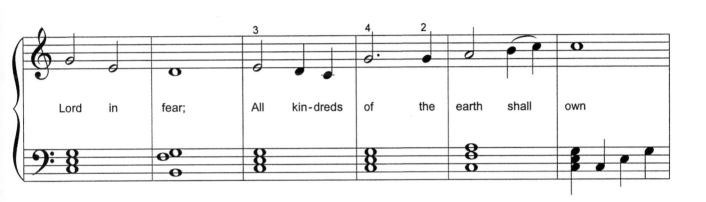

Lord in fear; All kin-dreds of the earth shall own

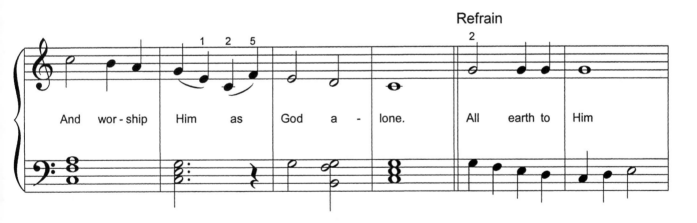

Refrain

And wor - ship Him as God a - lone. All earth to Him

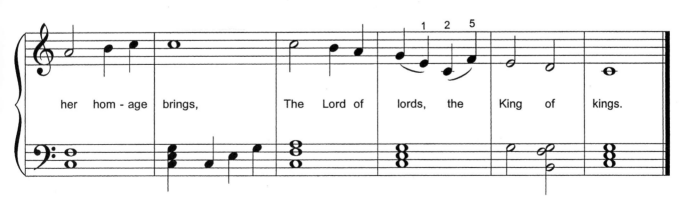

her hom - age brings, The Lord of lords, the King of kings.

God and His Church

Psalm 132
Robert Lowry

1. Gra-cious Lord, re-mem-ber Da - vid, How he made Thy house his care, How he

vowed to seek no pleas - ure Till Thy house he should pre - pare. Lord, re -

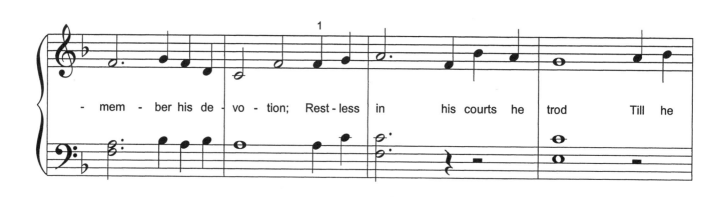

- mem - ber his de - vo - tion; Rest - less in his courts he trod Till he

found a hab - i - ta - tion Fit for Is-rael's might - y God, Till he

found a hab - i - ta - tion Fit for Is - rael's might - y God.

The Glory and Condescension of God

Psalter #306

Psalm 113
William B. Bradbury

1. Praise God, ye ser - vants of the Lord, Praise, praise His Name with

one ac - cord; Bless ye the Lord, His Name a - dore From

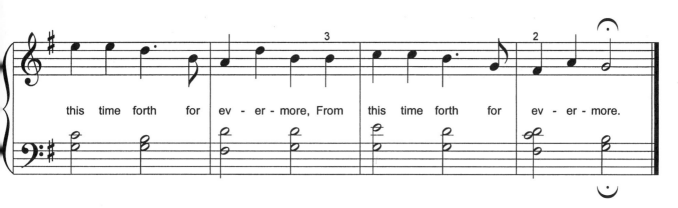

this time forth for ev - er - more, From this time forth for ev - er - more.

The Fearlessness of Faith

Psalter #71

Psalm 27
Anonymous

1. Je - ho - vah is my light, And my sal - va - tion near; Who

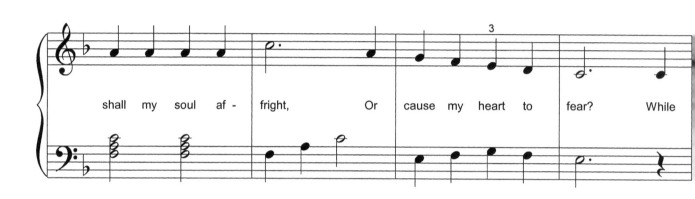

shall my soul af - fright, Or cause my heart to fear? While

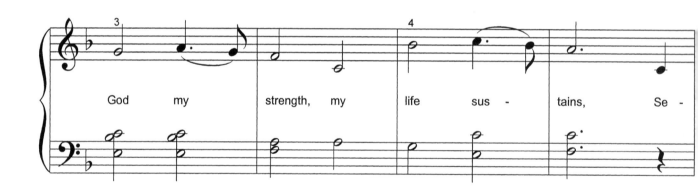

God my strength, my life sus - tains, Se -

- cure from fear my soul re - mains.

God Our Strength

Psalter #162

Psalm 62
Lowell Mason

1. My soul in si - lence waits for God, My Sav - iour He has proved; He on - ly is my rock and tow'r; I nev - er shall be moved. My hon - or is se - cure with God My Sav - iour He is known; My ref - uge and my rock of strength Are found in God a - lone.

Whole-Hearted Praise

Psalm 9
Arranged by Lowell Mason

Psalter #17

1. O Lord Most High, with all my heart Thy won-drous works I will pro-

claim; I will be glad and give Thee thanks And sing the

prais-es of Thy Name, And sing the prais-es of Thy Name.

The Blessedness of the Godly

Psalm 1
John H. Gower

Psalter #1

1. That man is blest who, fear - ing God, From sin re-strains his feet, Who

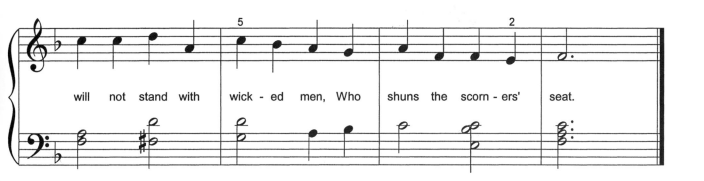

will not stand with wick - ed men, Who shuns the scorn - ers' seat.

Our Source of Strength

Psalter #36

Psalm 18
Arranged from Mozart

1. As Thou, O Lord, hast made me strong To o - ver - come my

might - y foe, So now to fight a - gainst the

wrong And con - quer in Thy Name I go.

Praise the Lord, Ye Lands

Psalter #418

Psalm 47
L. Bourgeois, 1551

1. Praise the Lord, ye lands; Na-tions, clap your hands; Shout a - loud to God, Spread His fame a - broad; Praise Him loud and long With a tri - umph song; Bow as ye draw nigh, For the Lord Most High, Ter - ri - ble is He In His dig - ni - ty; And His king - dom's girth Cir - cles all the earth.

Spiritual Aspirations

Psalm 25
Arranged by Benjamin Carr

Psalter #64

1. Lord, I lift my soul to Thee, O my God I trust Thy might;

Let not foes ex - ult o'er me, Shame me not be - fore their sight.

Yea, may none be put to shame, None who wait for Thee to bless;

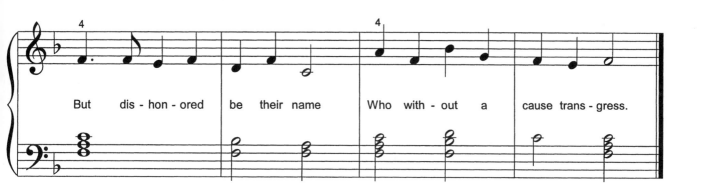

But dis - hon - ored be their name Who with - out a cause trans - gress.

The Look of Faith

Psalter #66

Psalm 25
George Hews

1. Ev - er are my long - ing eyes Tow'rd the

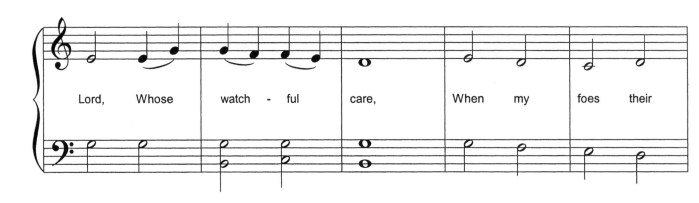

Lord, Whose watch - ful care, When my foes their

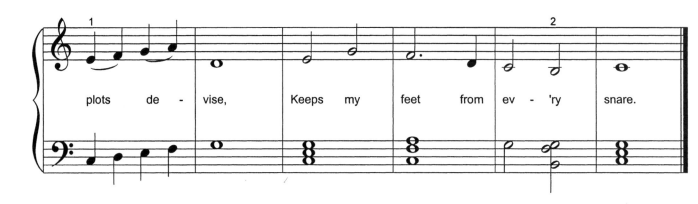

plots de - vise, Keeps my feet from ev - 'ry snare.

The Divine Law

Psalter #40

Psalm 19
George C. Stebbins

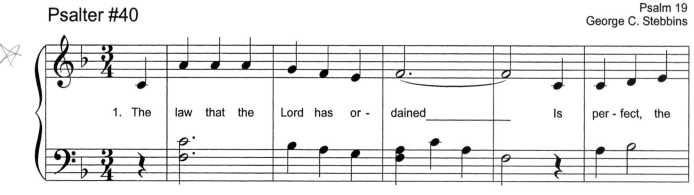

1. The law that the Lord has or - dained Is per - fect, the

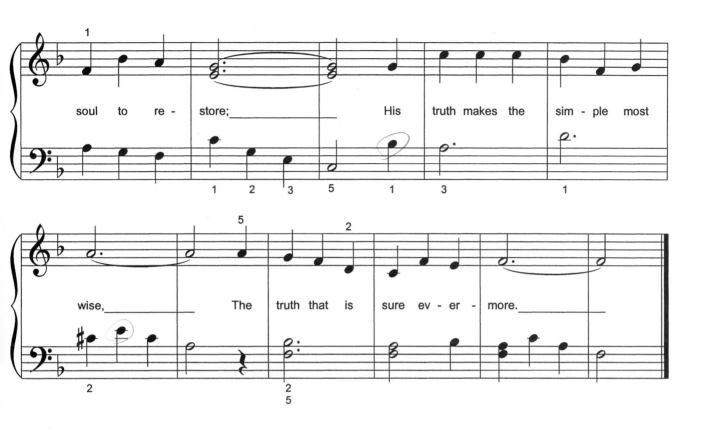

soul to re - store;_____ His truth makes the sim - ple most

wise,_____ The truth that is sure ev - er - more._____

Fellowship with God

Psalm 16
George N. Allen

Psalter #28

1. When in the night I med - i - tate On mer - cies mul - ti - plied,_____

_____ My grate - ful heart in - spires my tongue To bless the Lord, my Guide._____

Christ's Inheritance

Psalm 2
Lowell Mason

Psalter #4

1. O where-fore do the na - tions rage, And kings and rul - ers

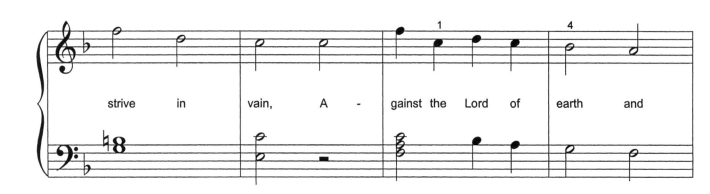

strive in vain, A - gainst the Lord of earth and

heav'n To o - ver-throw Mes - si - ah's reign?

Aspiration and Supplication

Psalm 25
Arranged from von Weber

Psalter #67

1. Lord, to me Thy ways make known, Guide in truth and teach Thou me;

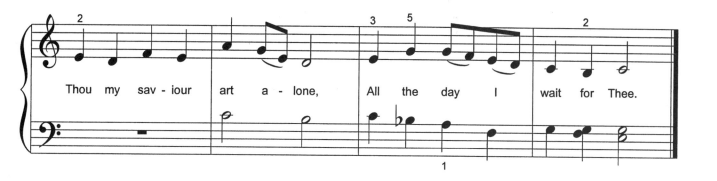

Thou my sav - iour art a - lone, All the day I wait for Thee.

Devout Prayers and Pleas

Psalm 86
John B. Dykes

Psalter #234

1. O Lord, my God, my joy - ful heart Will give Thee

praise for ev - er - more, For rich in grace to me Thou

art, My soul from death Thou didst re - store.

The Church of Christ

Psalm 87
William O. Perkins

1. Zi - on, on the ho - ly hills, God, thy Mak-er, loves thee well; All thy

courts His pres - ence fills, He de - lights in thee to dwell. Won - drous

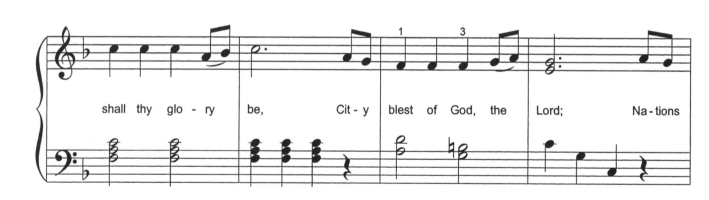

shall thy glo - ry be, Cit - y blest of God, the Lord; Na - tions

shall be born in thee, Un - to life from death re - stored.

The Divine Protection

Psalter #356

Psalm 125
Charles H. Gabriel

Brotherly Love

Psalter #369

Psalm 133
Arranged from Wallace

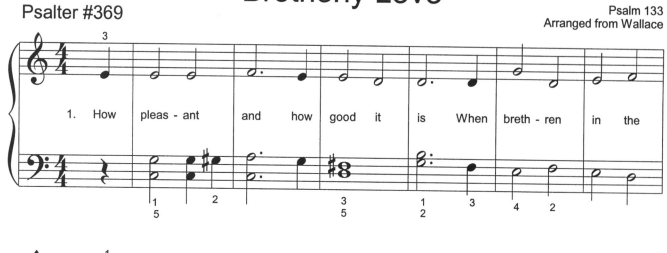

1. How pleas - ant and how good it is When breth - ren in the

Lord In one an - oth - er's joy de - light And dwell in sweet ac - cord.

The Doxology

Psalter #197

Psalm 72
Oliver Holden

1. Now bless - ed be Je - ho - vah, God, The God of Is - ra - el, Who

on - ly do - eth won - drous works, In glo - ry that ex - cel; Who

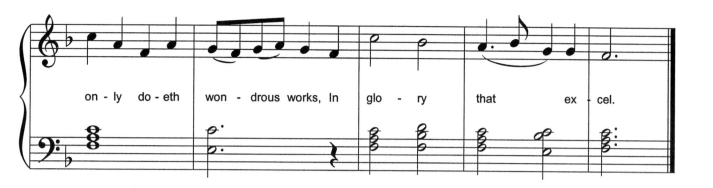

on - ly do - eth won - drous works, In glo - ry that ex - cel.

The Triumphal Ascension of Christ

Psalm 24
Charles H. Gabriel

Psalter #58

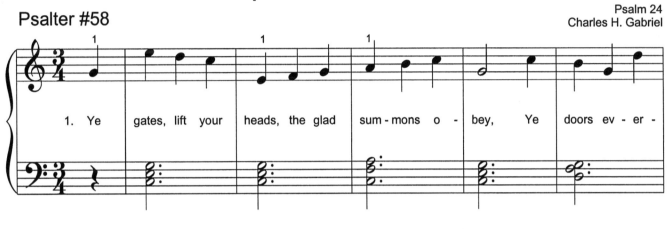

1. Ye gates, lift your heads, the glad sum - mons o - bey, Ye doors ev - er -

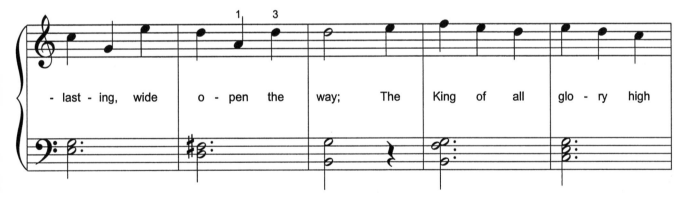

- last - ing, wide o - pen the way; The King of all glo - ry high

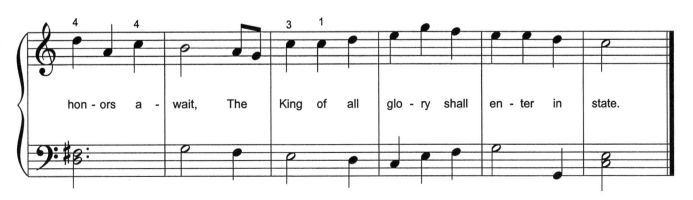

hon - ors a - wait, The King of all glo - ry shall en - ter in state.

Invitations to Praise

Psalm 135
Arranged from Haydn

1. Ex - alt the Lord, His praise pro - claim; All ye His ser - vants, praise His Name, Who in the Lord's house ev - er stand And hum - bly serve at His com - mand.

Redemption and Forgiveness

Psalter #362

Psalm 130
Charles H. Purday

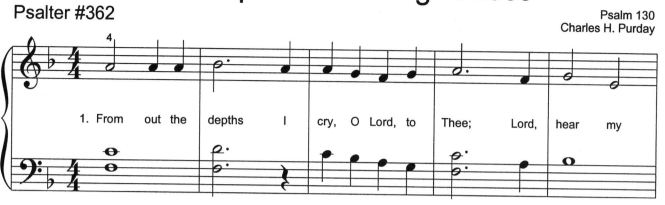

1. From out the depths I cry, O Lord, to Thee; Lord, hear my

call; I love Thee, Lord, for Thou dost heed my plea, For -

- giv - ing all; If Thou shouldst mark our sins, who then could

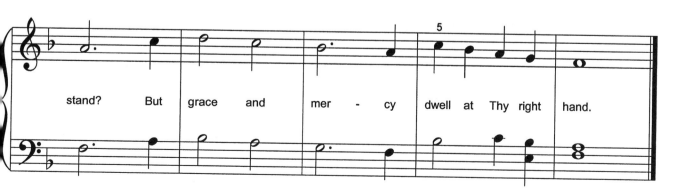

stand? But grace and mer - cy dwell at Thy right hand.

The Enthroned Christ

Psalter #200

Psalm 72
Arthur S. Sullivan

1. Christ shall have do- min - ion   O - ver land and   sea,   Earth's re - mot-est

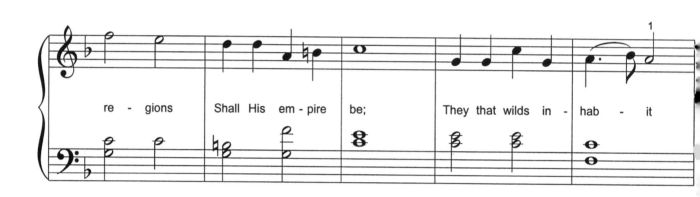

re - gions   Shall His em - pire   be;   They that wilds in - hab - it

Shall their wor-ship   bring,   Kings shall ren - der   trib - ute,   Na - tions serve our

King.   Christ shall have do - min - ion   O - ver land and   sea,

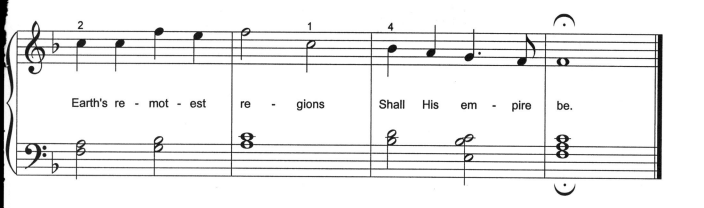

Earth's re - mot - est re - gions Shall His em - pire be.

The God of Providence and Grace

Psalter #86

Psalm 33
James McGranahan

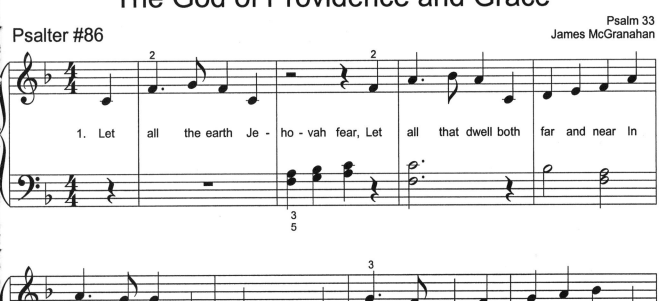

1. Let all the earth Je - ho - vah fear, Let all that dwell both far and near In

awe be - fore Him stand; For, lo, He spake and it was done, And

all with sov - 'reign pow'r be - gun Stood fast at His com - mand.

A Celebration of Divine Grace

Psalm 65
German Melody

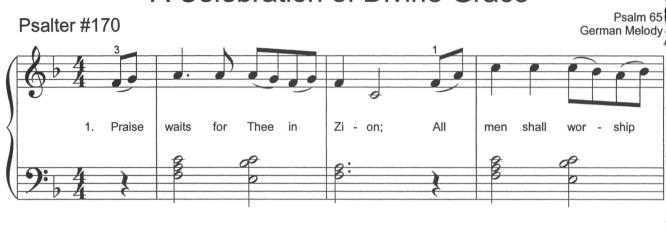

1. Praise waits for Thee in Zi - on; All men shall wor - ship

there And pay their vows be - fore Thee, O God Who hear - est

prayer. Our sins rise up a - gainst us, Pre - vail - ing day by

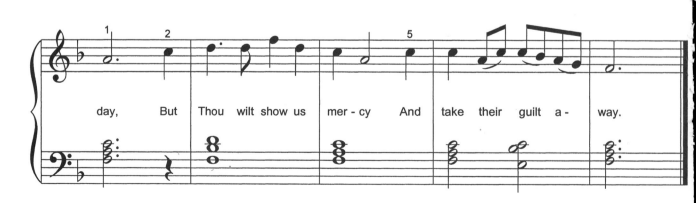

day, But Thou wilt show us mer - cy And take their guilt a - way.

Index of First Lines

Index of *Psalter* Numbers

The number on the left is the number in *The Psalter*. The number at the end of the dotted line is the page number of the simplified version in this book.